WHAT THE EMF?

HOW TO PROTECT YOUR HOME FROM EMF EXPOSURE, IMPROVE SLEEP, REDUCE ANXIETY, AND LIVE A HAPPIER, HEALTHIER LIFE!

RISA SUZUKI

WHAT THE EMF?

How to Protect Your Home from EMF Exposure, Improve Sleep, Reduce Anxiety, and Live a Happier, Healthier Life!

Publishing services provided by 

ISBN: 978-1-950043-00-2

Contact: Connect@RisaSuzuki.com, www.RisaSuzuki.com

Cover design: Archangel Ink
Interior design: Archangel Ink

Printed in United States of America

For more valuable resources and tips and to help you clear EMF fields in your home, I invite you to join me at www.RisaSuzuki.com.

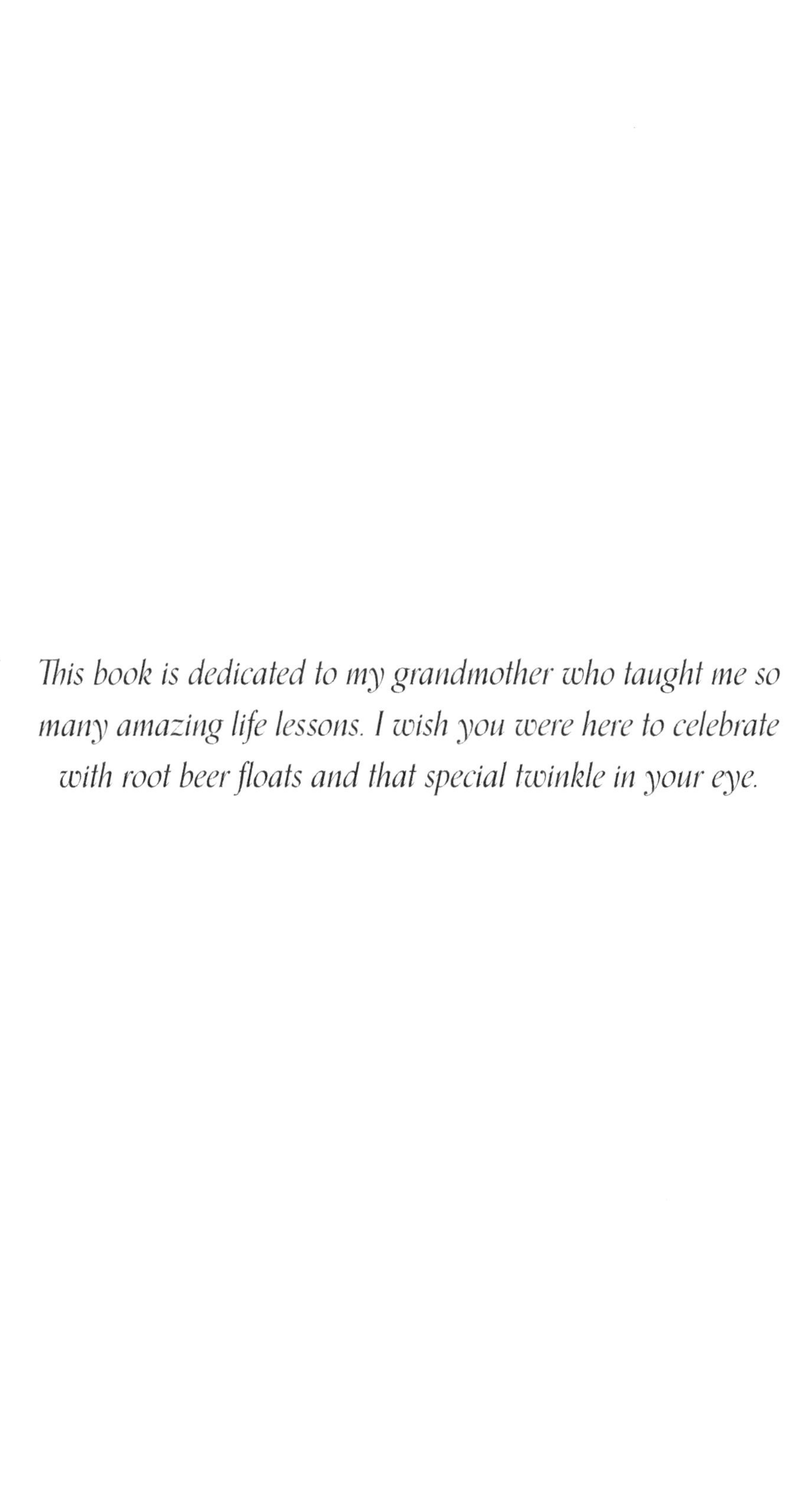

This book is dedicated to my grandmother who taught me so many amazing life lessons. I wish you were here to celebrate with root beer floats and that special twinkle in your eye.

FREE STUFF FOR YOU!

WHAT THE EMF? How to Protect Your Home from EMF Exposure, Improve Sleep, Reduce Anxiety, and Live a Happier, Healthier Life! is a practical, easy-to-follow framework to clear EMFs with foundational knowledge of the different types of EMF fields, guidelines for incorporating detoxifying and self-care techniques essential for managing EMF exposure, methods for recognizing the early stages of EMF symptoms and sensitivities, and strategies for managing exposure outside of the home.

I have four wonderful gifts just for you to jump-start your new project!

1. **WHAT THE EMF?** Master checklist will help you track your overall progress from start to finish. (Besides, we all like to check things off our list, right?)
2. **A Day in my Life Tech and Travel Tips:** Everything I do is in the book, but I still get the question "But what exactly do YOU do?" and this little booklet tells you how I use my phone and laptop and what I do to prepare when I travel.
3. **Creating a Healthy Home:** Air and Water are two other critical areas of creating a healthy home and supplementing your EMF knowledge, and here you'll learn what to look for in air and water filters to reduce the toxins in your home.
4. **Surprise Bonus!**

Get your free gifts by going to the link below:

WHAT THE EMF? Free Gifts

http://www.RisaSuzuki.com/WTEGifts

LOVE FOR THE BOOK

The book is such an easy read and is so practical. It breaks down complex concepts into small practical tips. Everyone can find something to start with, and it also provides answers to commonly asked questions and even some EMF myths. This is a much-needed book. We need a hands-on practical manual, from what type of measuring tools to use to how to avoid common misconceptions about EMF and protect yourself and your family, even to how to travel more safely. Risa also provides various checklists and teaches us how to be EMF detectives and how to prioritize and record the process. This is a great manual for anyone with any chronic illness or infection (like Epstein-Barr Virus) or compromised immune system because EMF can affect those the hardest, but I truly feel that everyone should read this book and learn how to curb our constantly increasing EMF exposure.

Dr. Kasia Kines, MS, CNS, CN, DCN, Doctor of Clinical Nutrition

This book is so comprehensive. Risa not only explained the technical aspects of EMF, but provided very specific steps as to what a homeowner can do to reduce EMF inside the home, how to use specific foods and self-care rituals to fight radiation, even how to handle EMF while traveling on airplanes and hotels, and so much more… It's very empowering… I was impressed with how thorough this book is! It will help so many people!

Lisa Fraley, JD, Legal Coach & Attorney

That this joins the all-too-sparse collection of books on this topic, holding a strong position introducing the uninitiated as well as more seasoned readers to the health impacts from this invisible man-made environmental pollutant. What surprised me the most was learning just how much we can also do to protect ourselves by making healthier diet and lifestyle changes!

Christine Zips, Investigative Health Journalist & Co-founder, WIRED SCHOOLS

Easy-to-read, "one-stop-shopping" for a practical, informative overview of EMF without being overwhelming. Reading this provided so many reinforcements of what I'm already doing for myself and my kids and reminders of a few other things that we can work on. ☺

Angela C. Thompson, Nurse Practitioner, owner of Matriarch Health and Wellness

Risa's book is everything you never knew you needed to know about EMF. Essential reading for people struggling with chronic health conditions and for anyone looking to improve their health, mood, productivity, and general well-being. I was surprised at the difference I felt after making just a few simple changes like turning my router off at night and sleeping with my phone on the other side of the room. Making small adjustments based on Risa's advice has helped me feel calmer during the day, improved my ability to focus in my work space, and transformed my ability to fall asleep, stay asleep, and wake feeling rested.

Sarah H., Environmentalist and Healthy Living Advocate

Since we cannot avoid EMF exposure, it is extremely helpful to have the knowledge about what creates these fields and how to reduce exposure. As an architect, I can use the information specifically in regards to the electrical systems, Wi-Fi, and utility drops to design in such a way that the all-important bedrooms are safer to sleep in. This book should be a lifesaver for people who are becoming aware that they may be sensitive to EMF and want to prevent this debilitating sensitivity.

Lotte Kragh, Architect

Thank you, Risa, for all the hard work and long hours getting EMF information to us. I can apply what I know now to my lifestyle so I can live a healthier life. Please continue to share your information with the world. You're touching lives!

Raquel Chin-Quee Murrow, Real Estate Broker

A highly comprehensive and ultra-practical handbook for navigating the complex EM field. I have already begun to apply tips. A DIY must to keep you doing it all right! Clarifies and answers many questions I have had. What a great tool touching all things of value in the land of EMFs.

Cathy Cohn, Certified Nutrition Consultant

This book offers very useful and much-needed material on the dangers of EMFs in a very informative and easy-to-read way. I enjoyed reading the book and learning more about this topic that I always encourage my clients and readers to pay attention to. I love the way Risa incorporates holistic advice into her EMF book—from sound healing to nutrition and crystal healing and more—this is much needed! Her many checklists are helpful and practical, and her room-by-room guidance is very useful. This is a wonderful book!

Rodika Tchi, MSc, Feng Shui Expert, TchiConsulting.com

A must-read for policy experts, corporate leaders, and medical professionals hoping to leverage the best that technology has to offer in ways that promote health and healing and protect against disease. Ms. Suzuki has years of experience in this area, guiding the expert and lay person alike as a consultant—which she has effectively translated into a casual writing style and easygoing tone that turns a complex subject into an engaging read.

Stephanie L Brown, Ph.D., Associate Professor, Department of Psychiatry, Stony Brook University

FOREWORD

I would recommend the book *WHAT THE EMF?* by Risa Suzuki for anyone that would like to be healthier and that would like to protect their brain and the brains of their family. I have known Risa Suzuki professionally for a number of years. Risa has done EMF consultations for many of my patients. As a result of Risa's knowledge and technical expertise, these EMF consultations have really helped numerous patients improve in their energy and cognitive issues. Risa's knowledge has also helped me to lower the harmful fields in my clinic and my home. I have learned a lot in conversations with Risa, and this has enabled me to make practical recommendations to my patients.

Risa gave a talk to clinicians on the biological effects of EMF, and it was very well received. It was very practical and well researched. Risa clearly understands the scientific and health issues. She also has shown a lot of expertise in making suggestions in remediation or decreasing the fields people are being exposed to.

This book is very practical in a number of ways. It will educate the reader in the types of fields that can be harmful. It will give suggestions on how to decrease harmful fields such as radio frequency fields from smart meters, Wi-Fi, and cell phones. It will also give information about harmful electrical fields and how to reduce them. It will educate the reader about common sources of EMF, what may be harmful, and how to take practical measures to reduce them.

This type of information should be important to anyone with children, as children are highly susceptible to the effects of EMF. Also it is very important to anyone with any neurological condition, as the brain can be affected by EMF. In fact, exposure to EMF can damage the blood-brain barrier, which can leave the brain open to autoimmune attack. In my Functional Medicine and Sports Medicine practice, I see a lot of patients with concussions, and decreasing EMF is a major recommendation for all of them.

Did you know that electric beds can produce very high fields? Did you know that Wi-Fi while you sleep is not good for your health? Did you know that smart homes and devices you talk to may be producing harmful fields? The information in this book is essential to help protect yourself and your family from harmful EMF, ELF, and RF fields. I think this book should be essential reading for anyone who wants to be healthy or who cares about the potential effects of EMF on family and friends. It should also be essential reading for healthcare providers.

I have authored a book and numerous chapters in books. This book is well written. It's a must read.

David Musnick, MD

Board Certified in Functional Medicine, Sports Medicine, and Internal Medicine

Bellevue, WA

www.peakmedicine.com

CONTENTS

INTRODUCTION

Shortly after I started writing this book, I was at an entrepreneur conference with a good friend and colleague who thanked me because me she and her kids had been sleeping better since they implemented a "no cell phones, TV, or computers" rule an hour before going to bed and an hour after getting up. In fact, one of her kids who occasionally needed to take melatonin to sleep through the night no longer needed to. She was astounded that one minor change could have such a noticeable impact in their lives.

Later that morning as we were doing introductions in the room, one of the hosts mentioned he'd heard (from our mutual colleague) that he and his wife should be turning off their cell phones at night to get better sleep.

I watched as everyone else in the room perked up and took note. Better sleep? Hell yes!

I don't even remember giving my friend that tip that helped her family, her colleagues, and now this room full of people.

This is why I love what I do. And it's random instances like this that remind me how much of a difference each of us can make, creating ripple effects in positive ways we could never imagine.

But I haven't always been that savvy EMF expert in the room.

Long before 4G existed, and even before 3G technology, I became aware of the invisible electromagnetic fields through an acquaintance who was studying how our cell phones, laptops, and electricity significantly impact our health and well-being. I'd been healthy and active my whole life, and anything relating to health always piqued my curiosity.

I had already done the "easy" things like turning my cell phone on airplane mode at night, hardwiring my internet connection at home, and limiting my Wi-Fi exposure. I knew I could be doing more, but I didn't know where to begin. I didn't have an engineering or science background or mindset to say the least! To make things more frustrating and overwhelming, the information and products I could find only seemed to make things even more confusing.

I wanted to take control of the EMF situation in my life, make the right decisions, and do the right things, so I enrolled in a three-year intensive program to become a certified Building Biology Environmental Consultant that would give me the EMF expertise I was looking for. My goal was to specialize in EMFs and help other people after I fixed my own environment. As much as I loved my career in technology, I'd had a childhood desire to somehow make a positive difference in the world, and as I learned about EMF fields, I felt my calling had landed on my doorstep.

The problem was I'd just moved back from Paris and was in a huge state of transition. I was living in an apartment, waiting for the lease on my house to expire so I could move back in, and I was also balancing a new full-time job with a new company. I hardly had any free time as it was, and I dreaded going back to school. The prospect of relearning biology, chemistry, and physics was intimidating because I was so terrible at them in high school, and I knew it wasn't going to be any easier this time around. I was investing a ridiculous amount of time, money, and energy into a little-known subject, but I knew at the core of my soul it was the right time. I needed to do this.

As much as I wanted to tell everyone about EMF fields and their health effects, I kept a low profile and studied every free minute I had for my exams, in-person seminars, and final project.

And then came the game changer.

[Enter music of impending doom.]

I started developing EMF sensitivities after I moved back into my house because something had changed outside. I wasn't able to get decent sleep, and I couldn't work in my office even though nothing had changed in my daily routine. In the blink of an eye I was exhausted every day because I couldn't sleep and woke up feeling wired and jittery. I got headaches and could barely focus well enough to do even the simplest things after an hour or two in my office. All of this even though nothing had changed in my life.

Suddenly, fixing my environment wasn't a choice.

It became a necessity to make the *right* changes if I was going to get healthy again and get my life back.

As I started chipping away at the EMFs in my environment, something didn't feel quite right, but I couldn't put my finger on it. Intuitively I felt a big piece of the puzzle was missing.

I completed my certification, cleared the fields in my house, and felt my symptoms improving. This freed up my schedule, and I was able to start doing holistic practices I had slacked off on since starting certification.

Suddenly, my triggers and sensitivities evaporated into almost nothing, and my lifelong allergy symptoms subsided. It seemed that clearing EMFs and adopting holistic solutions complemented each other perfectly. Not only did I feel better physically, but I felt balanced on the inside for the first time since fixing my environment. This was the "something more" piece I had been missing.

I wondered if my clients felt the same way deep down but just didn't express it when they were working with me.

So I decided to experiment.

I mentioned a few holistic solutions to my next client and saw her light up inside. She pounced on the information, wanting to know more and asking what else she could do. I started telling more clients and got the same reaction every time. They were eager to add in holistic solutions but hadn't made the connection to how they also fight against EMFs.

I decided to expand my holistic "toolbox." I went back to my certification curriculum and mapped health effects and symptoms to different holistic solutions so it was an organized approach and not all willy-nilly.

As people started feeling better and getting out more, they also experienced more triggers. Their home environment was cleaned up from an EMF perspective, but when they stepped out, they'd get exposed, have a reaction, and be back to square one.

That's when I realized another critical component needed to be included for managing EMF exposure. My clients were going through the same thing I'd already been through, and they needed to learn what had become a normal routine for me.

When my symptoms subsided and I was able to be out and about like normal again, I'd get triggered because of cell towers, antennas, and power lines around me. Then I'd go home and either feel sick immediately or the next day. I learned what to look for through trial and error, fine-tuned what symptoms to look out for, and identified what worked to minimize my recovery time when I experienced triggers. As I began incorporating this into my normal routine when I went out, I rarely experienced severe EMF symptoms.

This was the last critical step my clients needed to learn in order to manage their exposure and symptoms outside of the house and have go-to solutions to avoid getting sick every time they went out.

I'm so thrilled to be able to share all of the EMF gotchas, secrets, and expertise with you in the following pages. I hope you can take in these strategies with confidence, knowing they've been tested and implemented in my life and in the lives of many of my clients.

Here's to your EMF makeover and to creating a ripple of change in your own special way!

XO

Risa

HOW TO USE THIS BOOK

This is the reference book I wish I'd had when I was desperately searching for information. I didn't need any more convincing that EMF fields were a threat to my health, but I was beyond frustrated and overwhelmed, unsure what to do or who to listen to and I just wanted to get pointed in the right direction. I knew almost nothing about how EMF fields work, where to find them, what to do to make my home safer, or that there were other easy solutions available that would help my body counter the adverse health effects from these harmful fields.

This book is a departure from other EMF books. It fills a much-needed gap that I see on a regular basis: people need an easy, step-by-step framework to guide them through all aspects of clearing EMFs in their homes in addition to foundational knowledge of the different types of fields to take into account.

This book is written for readers who don't have technical knowledge, those who are new to EMFs. There are tons of illustrations, step-by-step instructions for each room, and guidelines to incorporate detoxing and self-care practices that are essential for managing EMF exposure.

My hope is this book will meet you wherever you are in your EMF journey with the information and answers you've been searching for.

This book is based on the process I developed from working with countless clients over the years. Science has never come naturally or easily to me, so it's always been important to me to translate and explain things so that even the most nontechnical person can understand and know what they need to do.

Part One explains what EMFs are, how they affect your health, and what different fields need to be addressed in your home. This is the basic foundation you'll need in order to do the best job making your home a safer environment. It walks you through how to find outside sources that are impacting your house and the options you have in addressing them. You will also learn the most common sources inside the home that affect your health along with the critical mistakes that almost all DIYers make simply because they don't know; you'll learn how to avoid making these same mistakes.

Part Two is what I consider the toolbox of secret ingredients that round out and complete the picture of managing your risk and exposure to EMF fields. These sections are equally important and include things like managing your exposure outside of the home, creating a technology plan, learning to recognize and manage EMF symptoms and sensitivities in the early stages, and finding solutions for supplementing your diet and health with nutrition and holistic practices that help combat the downstream effects of EMFs.

Part Three is the step-by-step process of counteracting the EMF fields inside and outside your house that are affecting your health. We start with the outside sources and then go room by room with specific checklists so you know what to look for and what to do, which removes all of the guesswork.

PART 1

BECOME AN EXPERT WITHOUT READING A TEXTBOOK OR BECOMING AN ENGINEER

CHAPTER 1

WHAT THE EMF?

When it comes to managing our health, we usually think of exercising regularly, eating healthy, and (more recently) limiting the toxins in our water and the products we consume.

But when it comes to managing our exposure to EMF fields from our electronic devices? Not so much. I include myself in this category because until it was brought to my attention, I never gave the subject a second thought.

The idea of EMF fields being toxic or dangerous to my health wasn't something I grew up with, which is the situation for most people today. The last time a government agency was tasked with looking at health effects from EMF fields was the mid-1980s. But they lost funding and it hasn't been restored. So it's no surprise there is a huge lack of information available.

We need to be proactive and take a precautionary approach when it comes to EMF fields.

There are many similarities to the tobacco industry in that for years, smoking was considered safe and even glamorous. It took years for the public to be educated on the health effects because of the industry dollars that supported the business. Until then, people had to take their own precautionary approaches.

The same is true of EMF fields.

While scientists, doctors, and industry leaders still disagree on the particulars, there is a growing body of evidence showing that EMF fields create numerous downstream health effects.

Electromagnetic fields, or "EMF" fields, are invisible. They fall into two main categories: natural and man-made.

Natural fields are naturally occurring as part of life and are necessary for our survival. While they are invisible to the eye, they can be measured with special instruments. The earth's magnetic field created by the North and South Poles is an example of a natural EMF field.

And we as humans also have a natural magnetic field that is a necessary part of our existence. All living things—including plants and animals—have their own natural magnetic field.

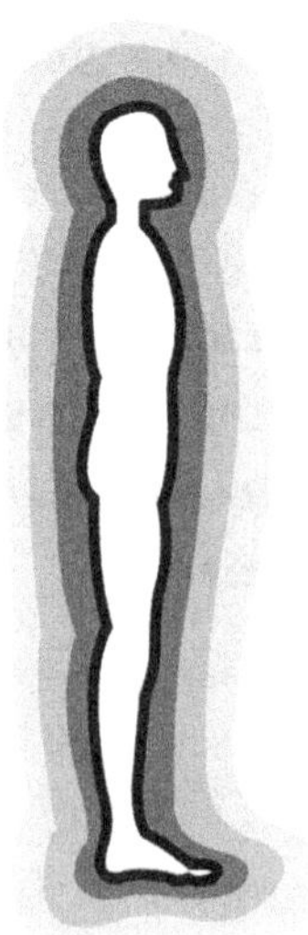

Man-made EMF fields are created by humans and therefore do not occur naturally. These fields are created by things such as power lines, electricity in our homes, our appliances and electronics, cell phones, and computers. These are the fields we're concerned about when it comes to negative impacts on our health.

These man-made EMF fields send signals that confuse the body because they aren't "natural" to us, and the body doesn't know how to interpret them. This can create those negative health effects, which we'll be covering in the following chapter.

Knowing what sources create EMF fields and managing your exposure is critical for managing and maintaining good health.

CHAPTER 2
HEALTH

If you have a sneaking suspicion the wireless technology in your home is negatively impacting your health, you're absolutely right. Your intuition is right on target!

"Long-term exposure to EMF (either prolonged or repeated or both) reduces your body's resilience to stressful forces in the environment."[1] Not only that, but the effects are also cumulative.

Below are some common health issues[2] linked to EMF field exposure that are cause for concern:

- Brain hyperactivity (ADHD or ADD)
- Autism
- Headaches of various types (migraines, throbbing, feeling a tight band around the head)
- Tinnitus
- Cancers and tumors
- Inflammation-related diseases such as allergies, asthma, arthritis, Crohn's disease, fibromyalgia, and neurodegenerative and cardiovascular diseases

In today's world where we find toxins in our food, air, water, and products, the body reaches a point where it can't take on additional toxins. That's usually when symptoms and sensitivities start to show up.

For example, if you're wearing a water-resistant jacket and standing in the pouring rain, at some point the jacket reaches its limit and starts to leak, so you end up soaking wet. The same thing happens with our bodies. At a certain point, the amount of toxins put into our body exceeds its limits, and symptoms and diseases start to show up.

EMF sensitivities and symptoms can show up very clearly, like if you use your cell phone and then your hand or wrist hurts or tingles immediately. Other people exposed to the same EMF fields may feel nothing.

Areas of Your Body Where You're Most Susceptible

- Brain: The side where you talk on your phone or wear a headset
- Central organs (heart, nervous system): Putting your cell phone in your bra, working on a laptop, and exposure to wireless transmitters and tablets
- Reproductive organs: Keeping a cell phone in your pocket, working on laptop on your lap, tablets (kids)
- Eyes and ears: Using headsets or wireless earbuds, cell phones, and laptops

Does EMF Exposure Affect Your Pets?

Yes! EMF fields absolutely impact our pets because they are living, breathing animals, and EMF fields can affect them in the same way they impact humans, which you'll learn in this chapter. In fact, because our pets are smaller than us, they can be impacted more than us.

How EMF Fields Affect Us

Below is a simplified explanation of what happens and how our bodies respond to EMFs regardless of whether you have sensitivities or not.

EMF fields are created from things like our cell phones, cell towers, electricity, and electronic devices.

The blood-brain barrier, which is a protective layer around our brains that prevents toxins from entering, is affected[3,4,5,6] by these fields. For example, when a cell tower or cell phone sends out a signal, our brain receives the signal but doesn't know what it is or how to interpret it.[7,8] As the brain tries to figure out what these signals are, the blood-brain barrier opens for a split second, and toxins enter the brain.

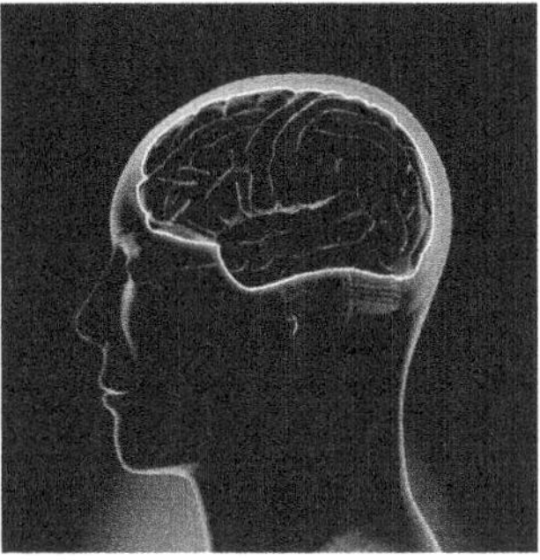

In the meantime, the body *still* hasn't figured out what these signals are.

The body concludes it's being attacked and triggers fight or flight (stress response)[9, 10, 11] and we hunker down, ready to defend against our attacker. As a result:

- Your body's resources are fighting this "emergency," but your body isn't designed to be under a constant state of stress, which creates long-term impacts.

- Your body produces more cortisol, increasing your heart rate and your breathing and affecting your respiratory and digestive systems. Glucose levels and fatigue can also result from the constant drain on your body.

- Your body starts to produce stress proteins within five minutes as a defense mechanism intended and accepted as a short-term benefit. However, over an extended long-term period, this actually has the opposite effect and reduces your body's ability to create those stress proteins to protect itself.[12]

When the stress response is activated, our cell membranes harden to protect against this mystery attacker. This means nutrients can't get into the cell, and toxins (e.g., free radicals) can't get flushed out. The cell becomes both energy deficient and nutrient deficient, and the DNA living inside the cells is impacted[13] by the free radicals because the free radicals prevent the DNA from repairing itself.

The cell continues its normal cell division (i.e., mitosis), and if the cell is in the first half of its life, it splits into two abnormal daughter cells, meaning the "damaged" DNA is passed down to the daughter cells.

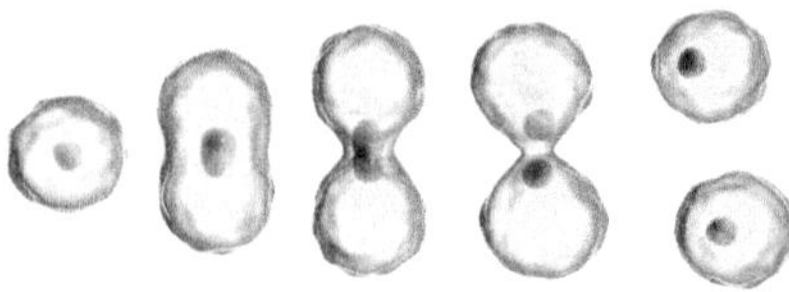

If the cell is in the second half of its life, the cell membrane dissolves and toxins are released into the bloodstream and into your body (also not a good thing).

This is why it's important to understand what's happening at a very basic cellular level. Just because you don't feel anything doesn't mean you're not affected.

EMF fields can also cause our bodies to raise our frequency or vibration to significantly higher levels than our bodies were designed for.

The body likes to be between 62 and 68 hertz[14] or cycles per second for healthy adults.

The frequency of wireless devices like cell phones is in the millions of cycles per second (MHz) or billions of cycles per second (GHz), which includes things like 5.8 GHz routers, baby monitors, or Wi-Fi, to name a few examples.

As you learned earlier, the body doesn't know how to interpret these man-made signals. As the body attempts to figure out these foreign signals, it tries to raise its frequency to match those higher frequencies in millions and billions of cycles per second, and this is called "resonance."[15]

If you've ever been next to a speaker that has a lot of bass and felt the sound vibrations going through your body, it's a similar concept.

If your cell phone is transmitting data (sending a picture, streaming a video, etc.), there is another factor. The data is transmitted at a much lower frequency (around 200 Hz). This data is sent in groups or "packets" in random order.

Cancer Connections

Because these man-made fields affect our bodies at the cellular level, scientists are studying the connection between EMF exposure and cancer.

The presence of micronuclei (instead of a cell having one nucleus there are a number of little nuclei) in blood cells is an indicator of DNA or genetic damage and is often a test used by doctors to identify patients who have higher chances of developing cancer. Living cells that contain micronuclei are not capable of repairing the broken DNA, and this deficiency will "likely lead to the development of cancer."[16]

Micronuclei are created twenty-four hours after exposure to different types of cell phone (e.g., radio frequency) exposure including digital and analog and exposure from personal communication systems instruments that can transmit both voice and data.[17, 18]

Currently, two types of EMF fields—*magnetic fields* and *radio frequency*—are formally classified by the World Health Organization as 2B (meaning that they are "Possibly Carcinogenic") and share the same category as lead, DDT, and chloroform, to name a few known toxic substances! In particular, radio frequency is associated with glioblastoma, which is an aggressive type of brain cancer tumor.

Other types of cancers[19, 20, 21, 22] that have been linked to EMF exposure include childhood leukemia, brain cancer, eye cancer, testicular cancer, and cancer of the parotid gland.

Brain and Cognitive Effects

EMF fields can literally trigger our brains into overload. When this happens, our cell membranes can leak and lose calcium, which in turn releases neurotransmitters, which can lead to brain hyperactivity.

This can exacerbate ADD, ADHD, or autism reactions or just affect your ability to sit down, focus, and get some work done.

Other health effects from EMF fields include Alzheimer's,[23, 24, 25] Parkinson's, and ALS.[26, 27] Slower response times[28, 29] have also been associated with EMF fields.

Tip: If you're sitting next to a router at full blast with wireless devices and accessories, and you're having difficulty focusing, try eliminating as much Wi-Fi as you can.

Many people also experience headaches of varying degrees of intensity such as:

- Throbbing headaches
- Feeling like the top of their head is being squeezed, or there is a tight band around their head
- More severe headaches
- Brain fog
- Pain at the temples
- Pain along the jaw or directly under the ears by the lymph nodes

Sleep and Fatigue Struggles

EMF fields can destroy your ability to get quality sleep, plain and simple. And quality sleep is essential for good health.

EMFs can drastically reduce your body's melatonin production,[30, 31, 32] which is critical for regulating and experiencing deep sleep cycles and fighting free radicals and diseases while you're asleep.

Lack of quality sleep also creates long-term chronic sleep deprivation, leading to other concerns such as weight gain and heart issues. Fatigue is another common side effect of EMF exposure—not only from lack of sleep, but also resulting from a constantly activated stress response.

Common sleep and fatigue symptoms from EMFs include:

- Feeling wired or jittery when waking up
- Feeling fatigued and exhausted when waking up even though you went to bed early (or just feeling like you've hardly slept)
- Waking up with headaches
- Not being able to sleep through the night
- Feeling constantly drained (especially after being around computers)

Metals Toxicity and the Human Antenna Effect

If you have heavy metals toxicity, it is important to minimize your exposure to EMF fields.[33] In general, metal attracts and conducts current. For example, the wiring in your house conducts current from the breaker box to the outlets to provide electricity for your electronics. Similarly, the metals in your body can act as an antenna by attracting the fields to you and then conducting current through your body.

If you have amalgams or metal surgical implants, EMF fields can cause these metals to leach into your system.

Children's Risks

Children, especially infants and toddlers, are considered higher risk when it comes to EMF health impacts because their skulls are much softer and easier for the fields to penetrate. Their bodies are also much smaller, so they absorb a higher percentage of radiation. Because they're still developing and growing quickly, their cells are rapidly dividing and increasing, and if the cells are damaged from radiation exposure, the multiple daughter cells are also damaged.

Dr. Om Gandhi found the following differences in the SAR (specific absorption rate measured by milliwatts per kilogram) of radiation:[34, 35]

<u>Brains</u>

7.84 for adults
19.77 for ten-year-olds
33.12 for five-year-olds

<u>In the eye fluid</u>

3.3 for adults
18.38 for ten-year-olds
40.18 for five-year-olds

<u>In the eye lens</u>

1.34 for adults
6.93 for ten-year-olds
15.6 for five-year-olds

<u>Connective tissue in the eye</u>

1.77 for adults
9.8 for ten-year-olds
19.69 for five-year-olds

Some statistics to consider:

- Exposure from cell phones can penetrate a child's skull up to four inches.[36]
- Children can absorb twice as much radiation as adults.[37]
- Malignant brain tumor risks double for people who have used cell phones for ten years or more if they use them on one side of the head for most of the time.[38]
- Users who start using cell phones in their teen years or earlier increase their risks for brain cancer by 420%.[39]

Recap

Here's what you've learned in this chapter:

- ✓ How our body responds to EMF fields
- ✓ What happens in our bodies at a basic cellular level
- ✓ How the frequency of our bodies rise to unnatural levels from EMF fields (resonance)
- ✓ How EMF fields can affect our ability to think
- ✓ How EMF fields can prevent us from getting quality sleep
- ✓ Which EMF fields are classified as cancer-causing
- ✓ How metals toxicity can affect your sensitivity to EMF fields
- ✓ Why children are at higher risk for EMF fields

Now that you've learned a little more about how EMF fields affect our bodies and some of the health consequences that result, you're going to learn about the different types of fields in your home so that you can address them.

CHAPTER 3

THE FIVE FIELDS TO ADDRESS IN YOUR HOME

In this chapter, we'll cover foundational knowledge about the different types of EMF fields. You'll learn how they work and look at examples to better help you identify them in your environment as you start your own remediation process.

The five EMF fields you need to know are:

- AC Direct
- AC Magnetic
- Radio Frequency
- Dirty Electricity
- Net Current

These fields have different units of measurement (milligauss, volts per meter squared, etc.) and are measured with different types of instruments.

Each field can exhibit one or all of the following characteristics:

- Passes through materials such as walls, windows, and ceilings
- Is partially absorbed into materials
- Bounces or deflects off walls, ceilings, or floors

Most people think that you need to get rid of your electronic device to reduce the fields, but usually it looks more like this:

- Remove the source or item that's creating the fields from your environment.
- Create safer distances between yourself and the source.
- Switch out the product or item for a lower-radiation one.

- Reduce your overall exposure.
- Use EMF-specific products that can protect you from the fields.

Many of the sources that create EMF fields create more than one type of field, as you'll see later in the book.

Before we can dive into these five fields, though, we need a primer on frequencies. EMF frequencies are important to understand because the different EMF fields have different frequency ranges. And as we learned in the previous chapter, your body tries to raise your frequency to meet the EMF field frequencies.

EMF Frequencies

Have you ever started to read an EMF article and gotten completely lost when it started talking about different frequencies? If so, you're not alone.

As a side note, if you ever decide to purchase EMF instruments in the future, understanding the concept of frequency will also help you evaluate different instruments because they often specify the frequency ranges that the instrument covers for the specific field being measured.

EMF frequencies are measured in what's called hertz (Hz). Hertz is measured in the number of cycles per second. For example,

> 1 hertz = 1 cycle per second

Or:

> It takes 1 second to complete one cycle

The electricity in our homes cycles at 60 hertz, or 60 cycles per second. That means it takes one second to complete 60 cycles when it comes to the frequency of our electricity.

The difference between 1 hertz and 60 hertz might look like this:

Time Duration = 1 second

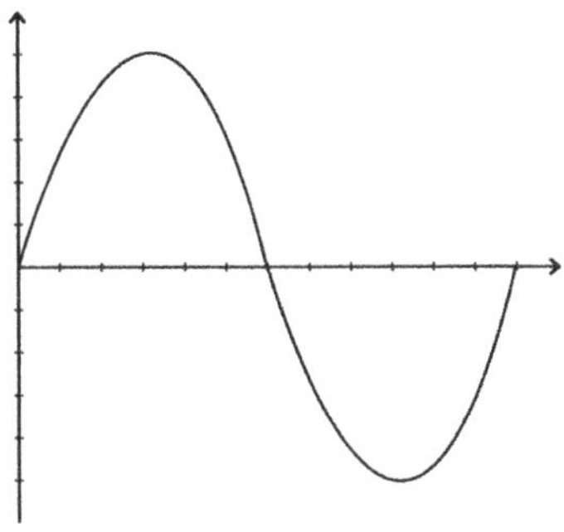

60 hertz

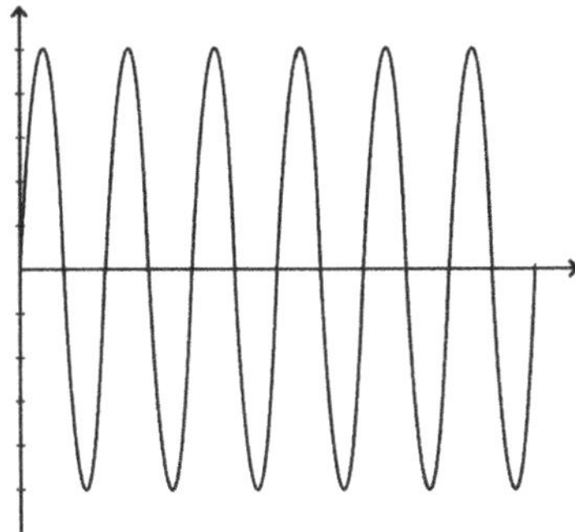

The lower the hertz (frequency), the bigger the "waves," and the higher the hertz (frequency), the smaller the waves.

You can also think of it like waves in the water—think of the huge rollers that can be several feet high in the middle of the ocean compared to the smaller waves that might be created by a speedboat on a lake.

Now we're going to apply this to EMF fields.

Below is a list of EMF fields and their associated frequencies (hertz) and examples of sources.

AC Direct (60 hertz)
Number of hertz = 60
Example source: electricity, power lines

AC Magnetic (60 hertz)
Number of hertz = 60
Example source: electricity, power lines

Radio frequency (2.4 megahertz)
Number of hertz = 2,400,000
Example source: cell phone, smart meters

Radio frequency (5 gigahertz)
Number of hertz = 5,000,000
Example source: Wi-Fi modems, Bluetooth

Frequencies also relate to our health; below are some examples of frequencies that are needed for the various parts of our body to heal. As you can see, the healing frequencies[40] are significantly lower than the man-made frequencies.

Nerve regeneration: 2 Hz
Bone growth: 7 Hz
Ligaments: 10 Hz
Capillary formation: 15 Hz

Taking this one step further and pivoting this view to specific electronic devices, here are some real-life examples you can probably relate to:

- Airplane power systems: 400 Hz[41]
- Airport body scanners: More than 300 GHz[42]
- Analog cordless phones: 900 MHz
- Automobile collision avoidance radar: 24 MHz and 77 MHz

- Bluetooth devices: 2.45 GHz
- Cordless DECT phones: 1.8 GHz (Europe), 1.9 GHz (US), 2.4 GHz, 5.8 GHz
- Deep brain stimulators: 130–185 Hz[43]
- Internet modems and boosters: 2.4 and 5.0 GHZ
- Metal detectors: 3,500 Hz[44]
- Microwave ovens: 2.4 GHz
- Mobile phone ranges in the US: 700 MHz, 800 MHz, 850 MHz, 900 MHz, 1,700 MHz, 1,800 MHz, 1,900 MHz, 2,100 MHz, 2,500 MHz[45]
- Mobile phone ranges outside of the US: 450 MHz, 480 MHz, 860 MHz, 900 MHz, 1,700 MHz, 1,800 MHz, 1,900 MHz, 2,300 MHz, 2,400 MHz[46]
- Smart meter cell phone band: 900 MHz
- Smart meter data transmission (your utility usage): 902–928 MHz and 2.4 GHz (varies by manufacturer and utility company)

Now that you know a bit about frequencies, we can move on to our discussion of the five EMF fields.

Field #1: AC Direct

The first field you need to know about is called an *AC direct field* (AC stands for *alternating current*). This type of field is created whenever there is a "hot" or active wire that has electrical current running through it. For example, it could be the wiring that's connected to:

- Your breaker box to an outlet or a light switch
- A cord from any electrical device to an outlet, such as extension cords, appliances, TVs, or cell phone or laptop chargers
- Power lines and cell towers

This is called the "wiring in the walls and cords" field and the strength of this field is typically measured in V/m (volts per meter).

This field is created from the electrical current in the wire or cord as it travels from one place to another.

For example, the current travels from the breaker box …

… to a light switch …

... or electrical outlet ...

... and the AC direct field is created along the same path as the wiring.

The EMF field extends outward from the wire, and the distance it extends depends on how much and how strong the current is.

This means an AC direct field is created along the entire wire even if there isn't anything plugged into the outlet.

If we take this one step further and plug a lamp into the outlet, the AC direct field continues from the outlet, through the lamp cord, and up to the lamp even if the lamp isn't powered on.

The same is true for a cell phone or laptop charger, TV, or any other electronic device that has two prongs (that means it's ungrounded).

Field #2: AC Magnetic

AC magnetic fields are *alternating current magnetic fields*. This field is created when items are powered on—they can be either battery-operated or electrically operated devices.

An example of an AC magnetic field is an electric toothbrush that is turned on when it is taken out of the charger. In this case, a magnetic field is created around the battery when it's turned on and also when the charging base is plugged into the electrical outlet.

This field radiates outward on all sides from the source and is measured in milligauss (how strong the field is).

AC magnetic fields always exist with AC direct fields when there is a cord or wire that is "hot" or has electrical current running through it.

In the breaker box example, the wire going from the breaker box to the outlet produces both an AC direct field and an AC magnetic field.

The same is true for a TV that is plugged in and on standby mode. It's not actually powered on, but AC magnetic and AC direct fields are created because it's still being powered by electricity.

This is also an example of how one EMF source (the TV) can create more than one type of EMF field.

Field #3: Radio Frequency

Radio frequency is probably the most widely known EMF field and is usually associated with Wi-Fi or cell phones. This is what's called *pulsed radio frequency* or *Information Carrying Radio Waves* (ICRW) because it can send packets of data (photos, streaming music, or videos).

There is another category of radio frequency, which includes AM/FM radio, TV, and microwaves and is called analog radio frequency. This type of radio frequency doesn't have the capability to send packets of data like pulsed radio frequency.

Unlike AC direct fields that travel from point A to point B, or AC magnetic fields that radiate outward, radio frequency behaves much differently. It's very dynamic, and it constantly changes direction and field strength in milliseconds. The strength of this field is measured by the amount of power density in either microwatts per meter square ($\mu W/m^2$) or milliwatts per meter squared (mW/m^2).

Imagine smoke traveling through doors, windows, and other openings, bouncing or deflecting off surfaces unpredictably, or going through walls and ceilings. This is how radio frequency behaves, which makes it difficult to predict where the radiation will travel to and where the fields start to fall off.

Pulsed versus Analog Radio Frequency

It's important to know the difference between the pulsed and analog radio frequency signals because, even though they're both categorized as "radio frequency," it's the pulsed radio frequency that many people are sensitive to and the explosion of pulsed radio frequency devices we are constantly surrounded by.

Analog Radio Frequency

Frequency = Kilohertz (KHz): thousands of cycles/second
Description: Sends signal (i.e., sound) across one frequency band

Pulsed Radio Frequency

Frequency = Megahertz (MHz): millions of cycles/second and Gigahertz (GHz): billions cycles/second
Description: Sends information (voice and data) across two frequency bands

Pulsed radio frequency uses two very different bands to send information:

- High frequency (Megahertz and Gigahertz) is used for sending voice
- A lower frequency band is used for sending the data packets in random order

Radio Frequency Risk and Exposure Constantly Changes

Radio frequency is constantly changing, which makes it difficult to predict your exposure and risk.

One of the reasons radio frequency is constantly changing is because it's based on demand. The number of people or devices sending and receiving data around you at the same time affects how much radiation is created.

For example, a cell phone is basically a transmitter that transmits signals out, which creates radiation, and receives data back, also creating radiation.

Let's say you have the following items enabled on your phone:

- Automatic email delivery
- Bluetooth
- Wi-Fi
- GPS

This means your cell phone automatically sends separate signals out and downloads data for:

- Email
- A device to pair with
- A network to connect to
- Your location

It looks something like this:

Every service enabled on your phone means a separate signal is sent out requesting data and creating radiation. When data is downloaded to your phone, radiation is also created. The more data or the bigger the files, the more radiation is created because more bandwidth is needed.

The more services you have enabled, the more radiation you're exposing yourself to.

When you're out in public, radiation levels increase exponentially because multiple devices and hotspots are constantly sending and receiving information.

For example, if you're at a restaurant with friends and you all decide to check your email or social media at the same time, the radiation cloud at your table will most likely surge at the same time.

Field #4: Dirty Electricity

Dirty electricity is created when there are harmonics on the electrical current in your home. It's found in just about every single home, and it's one of the least-studied fields, making it a challenge to study health impacts and conduct research.

The following are some examples of items that can create dirty electricity:

- Electronics with different speeds such as washing machines, kitchen blenders, or hair dryers
- Electricity coming into your home
- Switch mode power supply (SMPS) when chargers convert the electricity (AC to DC); used by cell phones, laptops, or tablet charger batteries
- Things that step down the power such as a dimmer switch or hair dryer
- Things that have higher frequencies than the electricity [e.g., a Wi-Fi modem or smart meter has higher frequencies (Megahertz or Gigahertz), which is overlaid on the electricity (60 hertz) when they're plugged in, which creates those harmonics]
- Smart appliances, smart switches, smart light bulbs
- Internet over power lines (also called broadband over power lines)
- Solar panels

Ideally, our electricity has a "clean" current represented below by a nice, smooth sine wave:

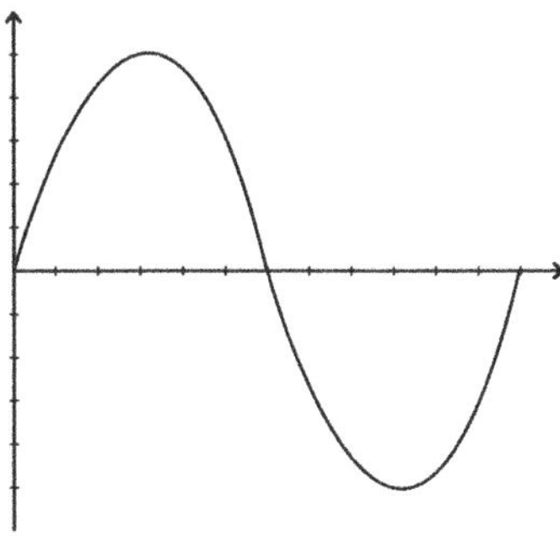

But the reality is, spikes and harmonics are created in our electrical current as a result of some of the items listed above, and our electrical current ends up looking more like this:

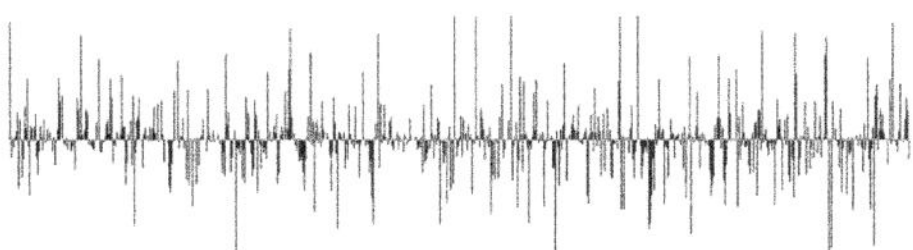

Important: Dirty electricity affects the entire circuit, not just a specific outlet where the source is plugged into.

Field #5: Net Current

Net current is basically extra current that's circulating throughout your home.

Electricity likes to complete a circuit, meaning that the amount that comes into the home should equal the amount that exits. When there is more coming in than going out or vice versa, the system is out of balance and you have net current.

Net current can circulate throughout the entire house because of the following:

- Grounding or wiring errors can create elevated fields all along the wiring.
- Current coming into the home on a metal water pipe circulates throughout the home on all the connected pipes.
- Knob and tube wiring creates magnetic fields as a result of the gap between the hot and neutral wires between the discs.

Ignoring net current detracts from other efforts to reduce your exposure from the other fields in your home. If you have net current in your home and shielding products are installed, it can make the situation even worse, so it's critical to validate and address this field.

EMF Field Cheat Sheet

Field #1: AC Direct

- The field comes from cords and wiring.
- The field moves outward from the source (i.e., wire or cord) and there must be current for the field to exist.

Field #2: AC Magnetic

- The field is created when a device is powered on (either battery or electrically powered).
- The field moves outward from the source (like dropping a rock in water that creates ripples).

Field #3: Radio Frequency

- The field is created when something is transmitting (either powered on or on standby) and the device can be either battery or electrically powered,
- There is pulsed and analog radio frequency.

Field #4: Dirty Electricity

- This is created when there are harmonics along the circuit where the sources are plugged in (cell phone, laptop, etc.).

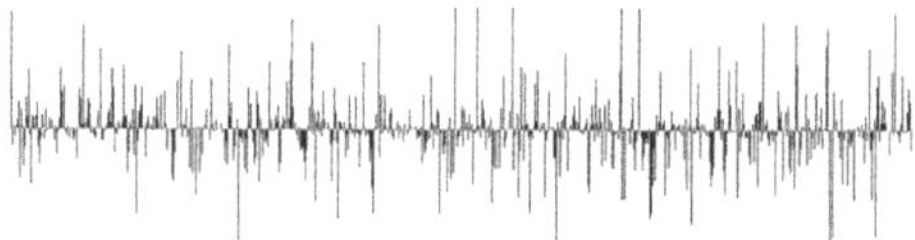

Field #5: Net Current

- This field is created when there is extra (net) current, and it can run throughout the entire house.

A Note about 5G Frequencies

You might be wondering what 5G is and how it fits into the EMF landscape. Similar to 2G, 3G, and 4G, 5G is another evolution in wireless technology with the potential to exponentially increase our radiation exposure. At the time of this writing, 5G has not yet deployed around the world, although test cities have been scheduled.

The biggest concern with 5G is the use of frequencies that have not been tested on humans for potential health effects. This is of serious concern given that these frequencies are in the sub-millimeter and millimeter wave range, which have been used as crowd control tactics because of their ability to create burning sensations on the skin. The licensed 5G frequencies are targeted to range from 600 MHz up to 48 GHz, and frequencies up to 71 GHz have been opened up but not yet licensed out around the world.[47]

Another concern is 5G antennas because the higher frequencies cannot travel as far as the lower frequencies can, which means the number of antennas are expected to increase exponentially, especially in neighborhoods.

Unlike the tall cell towers, 5G antennas can be easily mounted on utility poles, power poles, lights, and buildings because of their small size.

In addition to the antennas, 5G will also radiate down through thousands of satellites that started launching in 2018.[48]

Smart cities, the smart grid, and the Internet of Things (IoT)[49] are also key components of the overall 5G plan.

A number of cities and countries around the world have started to ask for health-based studies to be conducted on the impacts of 5G before deploying this technology or have simply decided to halt deployment until there is proof that 5G doesn't cause negative biological effects. The good news is that this is a growing trend, and increasingly more people are becoming aware of the health risks. However, it is still very much the exception rather than the norm.

Note: 5G mitigation most likely will require radio frequency instruments and shielding products. As more information is available, 5G solutions will be added to this book.

Recap

Here's what you've learned in this section:

- ✓ The five different types of fields that you need to know about in your home to remediate:
    - AC direct
    - AC magnetic
    - Radio frequency
    - Dirty electricity
    - Net current
- ✓ How these fields behave and examples of common sources
- ✓ The difference between the two kinds of radio frequency

CHAPTER 4

EMF SOURCES OUTSIDE THE HOME

It's critical that you take into account EMF sources outside of your home such as power lines and cell towers because they can directly impact the EMF levels inside. Sometimes the levels can be significantly high, depending on the proximity to your home, how strong the fields are, and where the home is in relation to these sources. The first step, though, is knowing how to find the external sources that are impacting your home.

This section gives you the foundation of what you need to know to assess your situation and reduce your impact from outside sources such as:

- Power lines
- Utility service drops
- Utility poles, transformer buckets, and lamps
- Cell towers
- Smart cells (also called small cells or boosters)
- Bus lines
- Smart meters
- Solar panels

Power Lines

Power lines are the electrical lines that deliver electricity to your home. These are either under the streets and sidewalks or overhead, which is what you see in most neighborhoods today.

Overhead power lines attach to the utility poles with lines or cables running from the utility pole directly to the house, which provides the electricity to the home.

Underground power lines under the sidewalks or street in front of homes are usually found in pockets of older neighborhoods.

Both types of power lines create AC direct and AC magnetic fields.

There are pros and cons for both types of fields:

Overhead

- Pro: Very easy to see
- Pro: Characteristics such as height and number and thickness of wires, etc. indicate stronger or weaker fields
- Con: Fields tend to create higher background levels of AC direct and AC magnetic fields in the home because of stray fields from the wires

Underground

- Pro: Usually lower voltage and magnetic fields affecting the house
- Pro: Radio frequency background fields tend to be significantly lower because there aren't any utility poles or power lines to mount smart cells or other wireless boosters
- Con: Hard to tell how strong current is because lines aren't visible

Overhead Power Lines

Stray fields from overhead power lines can drop off as little as 20 feet away from the power line or extend a few hundred feet depending on how tall the lines are and how much current is running through them.

The amount of current goes up with taller poles, more wires, thicker wires, and bigger, more frequent silver disks. More current means stronger fields, and more distance is required before stray fields start to fall off. The stray fields fall away from the lines in an A shape (see below) and decrease in strength with distance depending on how strong the field is.

> It's more efficient for the utility company to send more electrical current than is needed, and as a result, stray fields from the power lines will occur.

What to Look For

- Height: The taller the poles, the more distance is required for the fields to drop off. There is a higher chance they will impact your house compared to overhead power lines with shorter poles.
- Location of the utility pole: Is it next to your house? Or across the street? Utility poles usually have a hub of wires because they

deliver power to more than one house. It's best for the utility poles to be as far away from your home as possible.

- Presence of silver disks on the utility poles: These silver disks indicate more current running through the lines. This means that the fields are significantly stronger and need more distance before they start to drop off in strength. The disks are usually located toward the top of the pole, so be aware of any second- or third-story floors with rooms near these.

- Step-down Transformers: These are the gray buckets that look like large garbage cans located on some of the power poles. Sometimes there's just one bucket on a pole, but there can be up to three buckets. These also vary in size—some are taller and bigger than others. These buckets basically step down and reduce the amount of electricity so it can be delivered to the house and consumed safely.

Underground Power Lines

Underground power lines can also create stray fields, which usually drop off anywhere from four to six feet away from where the cables run.

Typically, neighborhoods with underground power lines have much lower background AC direct and magnetic fields, which translates to those fields being much lower inside the home.

The catch is if there are elevated magnetic fields from the lines running underground, and the only way to detect them is to take measurements with an AC magnetic field meter.

One advantage of underground power lines is that you don't have to worry about cellular antennas and small cells mounted on the utility poles or overhead power lines. This means the radio frequency levels can also be significantly lower, too.

What to Look For

- The service drop pedestal: Is it a short square stump or a big green box? Or do you see both? Ideally, you have only the short square stump because the big green box means that it's also powering other houses and creating elevated fields.
- Location: Where is it? Is it fairly close to the house or a distance away from it? These should be as far away as possible (ideally, at least 20–30 feet for the square stumps).

Service Drops and Breaker Boxes

Service drops are where the power lines attach to the meter and distribution panel and bring electricity into the house. Every house has a service drop regardless of whether the power lines are overhead or underground, and these are mounted on the outside of the house or building.

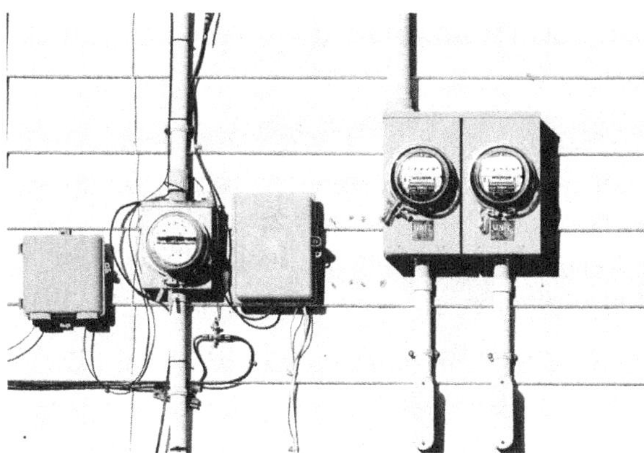

The breaker box is usually located on (or within a few feet of) the interior side of that same wall.

It's important to know where the service drop and breaker box are located because stray AC direct and magnetic fields are created in those locations, and options are very limited when it comes to protecting yourself against these fields.

Stray fields created from service drops and breaker boxes *also* extend vertically up or down from where they are located and impact those spaces as well.

Q: Can a licensed electrician move a breaker box?

A: Usually you can, but it means dismantling the current drop and possibly replacing older analog utility meter with a digital or smart meter, so it's best to research this beforehand. The best place to move it is an exterior building like an unattached garage or shed, and the second-best option is to install it on a wall in a room where you spend little time.

Note: Gas mains are another service drop to take note of by location because these often transmit your usage via wireless signal to the utility company.

Cell Towers and Antennas

Cell towers and cell antennas are the biggest outside contributors of radio frequency coming into homes. Most of them have "boosters" installed with them, which boost the cell signals and radiation. A number of studies have indicated increased health effects[50,51] including cancer in people who live in proximity to cell towers, which is why it's important to assess how your home is impacted.

Cell towers are the large steel towers or monopole structures that usually have multiple layers of cell panels like the one pictured below. They can also be existing radio towers that have more than one layer of cell panels. Usually these range from a hundred feet to several hundred feet tall and are easy to spot. The "boosters" are the square boxes above or below the cell panels.

Cell antennas are usually shorter in height and more commonly seen mounted on commercial building rooftops, around the exterior top floors of buildings, and on utility poles. Because these are smaller, they can be a little harder to notice to the untrained eye. They can also be painted a similar color as the utility pole or camouflaged to blend in with trees.

Cell tower radiation behaves like light from a flashlight (see below). At the source (the bulb of the flashlight), the field is the strongest and then radiates outward while increasing in vertical height. As it increases with distance from the bulb, the light and intensity decrease with distance. Cell tower radiation behaves the same way; the field strength and radiation levels will drop off with distance. The distance required for the radiation levels to drop off depends on how strong the signals are (information the cell phone companies keep confidential).

Remember: Radio frequency signals from cell towers are designed to travel several miles, not just several feet. This makes assessing your impact difficult if you can't see them from your house.

When you look at cell towers and antennas near your house, take note of the number of tiers, panels, and boosters. Also note how big the panels are because these indicate how much radiation is being generated.

If you have more than one floor in your home, and a cell tower at a higher elevation in any direction, you most likely have radiation coming through the ceiling of the top floor. This usually means a bedroom. If this applies to you, then your sleep is most likely being affected by radiation coming in through the ceiling.

Windows don't provide any protection from cell tower radiation, and skylights or windows facing the direction of cell towers above or below you present risks for radiation coming directly through the glass.

Myth: If you live a quarter mile or more away from a cell tower, you're "safe." In the earlier stage of cell towers (circa 2008), a distance of a quarter mile from a cell tower was considered safe. However, advances in technology and the ability to transmit the signals over longer distances with more power means that reference point is no longer accurate.

The two places to avoid when it comes to cell tower proximity are:

- In direct line of sight from anywhere in your house
- Below a cell tower

If you're in direct line of sight, you are constantly bombarded by radiation, whether it's through the windows, the walls, the ceiling, or all of the above.

The radiation is stronger the closer you are to the source, and the fields drop down vertically, so if you are below a cell tower, radiation will come in through your ceiling, windows, or walls.

Myth: It's better to live away from the city to reduce your impact from cell towers and power lines. Although this might seem like a good idea, this is not actually true. In fact, impacts from cell towers outside the city can be worse! Towers outside of the city must send the signals over longer distances to the next tower, and the signals can be much stronger. And in order for the signals to travel without being obstructed, they are usually at the top of very tall hills and peaks, meaning they are impacting the areas beneath them.

Find and Assess Cell Towers Impacting Your Home

Antennasearch

A good online tool for finding cell towers and antennas (in the US) is Antennasearch (www.antennasearch.com), which is free and accessible to anyone. Simply enter the address and it will show all registered cell towers and antennas within a two-mile radius.

The search results will tell you the tower's location, its height, which carrier is using it, and the distance from the address entered, if available. It may also show any pending permits for cell towers that are not yet built.

Note: This tool is what I consider a good indicator, but it's not always 100% accurate. In some instances, cell antennas aren't reflected in the Antennasearch results. It's always a good idea to drive around and validate the Antennasearch results.

Architecture of Radio

The other helpful tool is Architecture of Radio, a mobile application available on Apple or Android that you download and install on your phone or tablet.

The downside is you need to be connected to a wireless network with GPS enabled in order to use it. The benefit is that it shows real-time data not only for cell towers, but also antennas, hotspots, routers, and satellites.

This comes in handy if you're looking at a house to move into or you're just out and want to know what's around you that you can't already see. When I use it, I turn on Wi-Fi and GPS, launch the app, and use it. Then I turn them off when I'm done.

Small Cells

Small cells are small, compact units that are usually mounted on utility poles and power lines. They transmit radio frequency continuously and easily impact any of the surrounding homes because they're in such close proximity.

These come in all shapes, sizes, and colors and can be more difficult to see and identify. Some of them have cooling fans built in while others look more like a router with antennas.

These can be problematic for windows that directly face them, even on the second or third floors, especially in the evenings when people are home on their computers or streaming TV and videos and the radiation levels are higher.

Optional: If you have small cells within three or four houses of yours, you may want to consider taking radio frequency measurements both during the day and in the evening to see how much radiation is coming into your home. Once you have accurate measurements, you can decide what course of action to take, whether it's changing how those rooms are used or implementing shielding options.

Smart Meters

Smart meters replace the older analog-style meters (pictured below) that require someone from the utility company to come to your house and manually record your usage once a month.

Smart meters are digital utility meters that monitor how much electricity you use. They collect and send data to the utility company with wireless signals every twenty seconds to every few minutes, depending on the settings decided by your utility company.

Smart meters continuously broadcast pulsed radio frequency, and they transmit the data usually in bursts of milliseconds. These operate in the same frequency as our cell phones, and the radiation extends outward from the meter, but it also goes inward through the wall it's mounted on. It is also very easy for radiation to go through any nearby windows and affect floors above or below where these are installed.

In addition to the associated health effects from the radiation, there are numerous instances where smart meters have been linked to starting fires.

Smart meters also create dirty electricity, which can circulate throughout the entire house, because radio frequency is a higher frequency (MHz or millions of hertz) than the electricity (60 Hz), creating harmonics.

If you live in a neighborhood where houses are close together, you need to consider where your neighbor's meters are installed and if they're pointing toward your house.

Smart meters have what is called *two-way communication*, meaning that it sends information to the utility company, and the utility company can monitor and control your usage from their end as well, such as metering your usage or shutting off your electricity remotely.

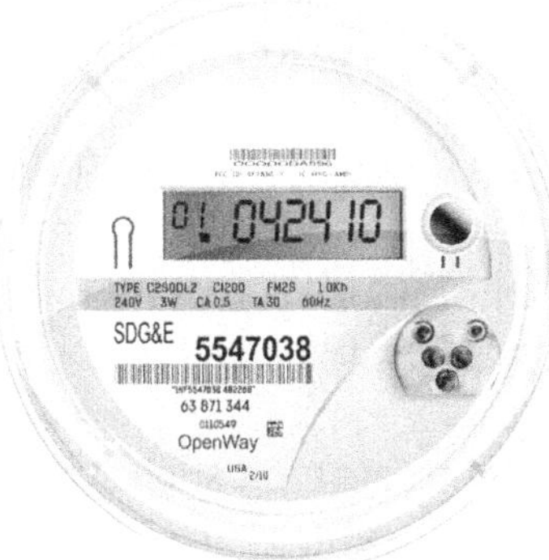

Having a smart meter installed on your home is the same as living 200–600 feet from a cell tower,[52] and that's based on data from 2013!

Apartment buildings, condominiums, and townhouses are susceptible to higher exposure because banks of smart meters can be installed in various configurations, including the following:

- All smart meters are installed at one location.
- Smart meters are installed every floor (sometimes one location on the floor and sometimes in a few locations per floor).
- Smart meters are installed every few floors.
- Smart meters are installed inside each unit.

Note: If you have had any electrical updates or remodels, your old traditional analog meter may have been replaced with a smart meter, so be sure to check if you have one.

Privacy Concerns

Smart meters create privacy concerns because the detailed usage data is tied to individuals, which can be used for marketing purposes if sold to a third party. As increasingly more smart appliances come with their own chips, they can send their usage data to the smart meter, providing even more detailed usage information.

Do Smart Meter Guards Work?

Smart meter guards can be purchased, and these will help reduce the radiation emitted from the front of the meter. The age of your smart meter and whether it's a stealth meter determine a guard's effectiveness.

Most of the newer smart meters emit such strong signals that a fairly high level goes through the shield. The older meters and stealth meters transmit less radiation and have weaker fields, so shields tend to be more effective with these.

Smart meter guards are beneficial if there are windows near the smart meter, whether they are on the same floor and next to it or a floor or two above the meter, because the radiation in all these examples can easily go through the windows.

Stealth Meters

A *stealth meter* is a hybrid between an analog meter and a smart meter.

It has the analog face on the front of the meter with the five dials but has a wireless chip that sends your utility data to the utility company. In other words, it looks like an analog meter, but it's not. These are called *one-way communication meters* because they can only send your data one way to the utility company.

Unlike with a smart meter, the utility company cannot send data back or control your usage from their end, such as metering your usage or shutting off your power.

These meters tend to create less radiation than a smart meter, usually around 200 µW/m^2, but they still send out continuous signals. They can be mounted in groups for apartment and condominium buildings as well.

The easiest way to identify a stealth meter is to see if the word "Cellnet" is imprinted on the face of the meter. If it's there, then it's a stealth meter.

Smart Meter Resources

Your local smart meter group is a great resource because it will be current on the existing and pending regulations for your city and will be able to inform you about what options you have.

Smart meter gotchas: There are some instances where digital meters are deployed, but they're not sending data wirelessly yet. Or maybe smart meters haven't been deployed to your neighborhood. This can mean that an opt-out solution may not be in place because a decision hasn't been made, so it's important to find out what your status is.

Measuring Smart Meters

If you want to measure smart meters, you will need a radio frequency meter with a peak hold feature (more on this in the bonus chapter toward the end of the book) built into it. Smart meters send out signals in bursts of milliseconds, which is too fast for a meter to capture and display, making it extremely difficult to get an accurate reading.

The peak hold functionality captures this so you can see the highest readings and get accurate measurements.

Important: Spend as little time as possible in front of the meter and stand about three feet away to capture an accurate measurement. Don't forget to take readings on the inside where it's mounted and where any neighboring smart meters are pointing at your house.

Solar Panels

Solar panels are a great solution for reducing your footprint and allowing you to know how much electricity you are consuming.

Unfortunately, solar panels create harmful EMF fields. Every solar panel has an inverter in the middle of the panel. The inverters take the energy from the sun and convert it into the electricity for our homes.

These can create the following issues:

- Inverters can't be turned off (unless the panel is completely covered with a material the sun can't go through).
- Inverters can cycle every twenty seconds to every few minutes, depending on the settings.
- Inverters create dirty electricity unless a special clear sine wave inverter is used.
- Inverters create magnetic fields, which is problematic for the rooms directly beneath the solar panels.

The utility company must know how much electricity is being created and used, which means a smart meter is installed on the house in addition to the existing utility meter.

Recap

Here's what you've learned in this section:

- ✓ The most common outside sources that typically impact radiation levels inside the home
- ✓ The difference between overhead and underground power lines and some common characteristics of each
- ✓ How to assess the impact on your home from cell towers
- ✓ Two useful tools for finding cell towers
- ✓ Types of utility meters—traditional analog, smart meter, or stealth meter—and how to identify what type you have
- ✓ Solar power concerns

CHAPTER 5

HOW TO FIX SOURCES INSIDE THE HOME MOST DIYERS MESS UP

In this section you're going to learn common mistakes people make in mitigating EMF sources inside the home. You'll learn the correct mitigation steps so you can avoid making these same mistakes.

Bed Canopies and EMF Paint

You should never ever buy bed canopies or EMF paint unless 1) measurements have been taken for the different fields with a reliable meter, *and* 2) the measurements fall within the range of the shielding material specifications.

If you don't take these precautions, you could be in for an epic fail!

Here's what most people get wrong:

- They don't realize there's more than one EMF field they need to take into consideration (not just radio frequency).
- Materials typically only address one field.
- Shielding materials are only effective for a specific range, which is why you need to know if the measurements fall within the range.
- If the radio frequency fields are stronger than the material (which happens easily), the signal gets trapped, causing the fields to bounce around and increase the radiation levels by a multiplier of three or four.

- Shielding materials are conductive, and if the other fields (e.g., not radio frequency) are elevated, the shielding material increases the area for the fields to travel through, making things worse.

Bed canopies made from fabric designed to block radio frequency fields can be a quick and easy solution. EMF paint, on the other hand, takes some additional planning because in addition to painting the entire room, the windows, doors, or closets need to be addressed with a plan to prevent the fields from coming through.

Both are great options for shielding radio frequency, but they also create the potential for the most common mistakes that I see and hear about. While this book doesn't get down into the technical details of measuring and shielding scenarios, it's worth mentioning the criteria requirements. If you decide to look into either of these solutions, take the following precautions to avoid making common mistakes:

1. Take measurements for all fields beforehand so you know how strong the fields are (AC direct, AC magnetic, and radio frequency).
2. Ensure the measurements fall within the shielding material range and allow for higher fields in case the strength increases in the future.

3. Make sure radio frequency coming up through the floor is not an issue (e.g., if it's a ground level room or, if there are fields below, they are also blocked with a shielding material).
4. Be certain that AC direct and AC magnetic fields are as low as possible within one to two feet of the bed on all sides including the floor. **Note:** Wiring in the floor can create higher AC direct fields and use the shielding material to conduct through.
5. Ensure there's no metal in the bed frame, box spring, or mattress.

People who are in apartments or condominiums with floors above and below can face challenges because of shared walls and floors.

Building materials are also a contributing factor, where buildings with thinner walls and floors may have higher fields than newer buildings with concrete floors and thicker walls.

The fields can vary greatly between different buildings, which is another reason it's important to take measurements.

Turning off Bedroom Breaker Switches

Somewhere along the way you might have heard that turning off the breaker switches to your bedroom is good for you because it eliminates the fields from the electricity in the bedroom and will help you get better sleep. Right?

Wrong!

When your bed is next to "hot" or active wires, such as the wiring in the walls, EMF fields can jump onto your personal field and disrupt your sleep.

Most people make the mistake of hiring an electrician and installing a kill switch for the bedroom circuits, or they just manually turn them off at night. While it sounds good in theory to "kill" those fields running through those walls, that's not actually what happens from an EMF perspective. In fact, usually the opposite happens, and the fields increase when the bedroom breaker switches are turned off.

The simple reason is that rooms next to the bedroom are still powered by electricity. That means the shared walls, ceilings, and floors still have electrical current running through them because they're powering the other rooms. They usually share the same wiring path and are bound together with the same wires powering the bedroom.

When the bedroom breakers are turned off, it usually creates higher fields because the fields don't cancel out evenly.

The safest thing is to keep all the electricity powered on; otherwise, turn off all the breaker switches to eliminate the risk of creating higher fields in the bedroom (this, of course, can create issues for things like hot water tanks, refrigerators, or security systems that cannot be turned off).

If you are going to turn off breaker switches to a room, you need a good-quality AC direct meter that can measure less than .1 V/m or a body voltage kit. Either of these can be used to determine the exact combination of breaker switches that produce the lowest measurements.

Baby Monitors

Baby monitors and other wireless baby products produce significantly high amounts of radiation, and the lack of security built into baby monitors makes them easy for hackers to access.

Baby monitors are usually placed close to the crib and are battery-operated. This means that both radio frequency and magnetic fields are created and in close range. If the unit is plugged in, then AC direct fields and dirty electricity fields are also produced. The best option is to remove the monitor altogether, if possible.

Monitors that are "low-EMF" but communicate wirelessly are still creating radio frequency if they are in the MHz (millions of cycles) and GHz (billions of cycles) range. Monitors that have video capability create more radiation because video requires more bandwidth than audio-only monitors.

If the monitor can be controlled by a wireless device, a wireless signal has to be received by the monitor itself, meaning that pulsed radio frequency is created.

Personal Care Products

Personal care products used for brushing your teeth or cleaning your skin create extremely high magnetic fields—up to 200 milligauss or more when they're being used!

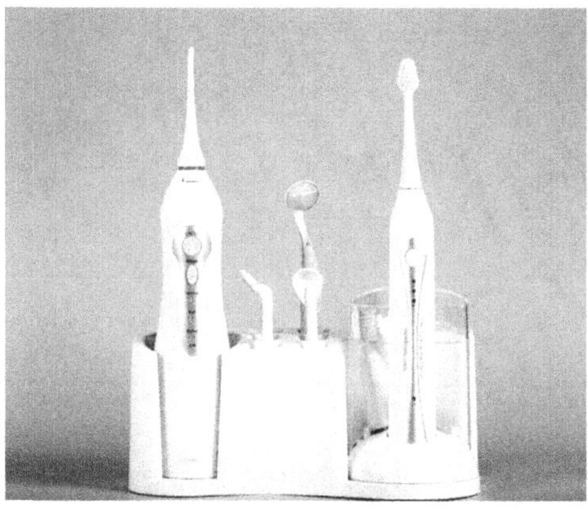

The main concern with these products is the extremely high magnetic field in such close proximity to your brain, even for a short period of time. You will need to weigh the benefits of using these versus the health impact from the magnetic fields.

And keep in mind that because these are battery-operated, when they are plugged in and charging, they create additional AC direct and magnetic fields and dirty electricity.

Cordless Phones

If you need to have a phone line for your house, cordless phones are convenient, but they produce extremely high levels of pulsed radio frequency as well as dirty electricity. In most cases, the satellite phones can transmit just as much radiation as the base stations, and both the satellite and base stations broadcast continuously.

The healthiest option is to replace a cordless phone with a traditional corded phone with a landline (not a VOIP phone). One of the challenges is that many phone companies are phasing out traditional phone lines. If you cannot get a traditional landline, the next best option is a hardwired VoIP (voice over internet protocol) phone that connects to your modem *as long as Wi-Fi has been completely disabled* on the modem. The catch here is that because it's a hardwired connection, additional satellite phones are not an option.

If you need caller ID or voice messaging, I recommend purchasing a business class phone, which may cost slightly more but will most likely have built-in caller ID, speakerphone, and voicemail.

You can purchase an older 900 MHz analog cordless phone if you absolutely need to have a cordless phone, but the traditional landline and hardwired VoIP are better options. Because it's an analog (you will need to validate this on the product description), it will not be transmitting data, which is slightly better, but it still transmits radio frequency.

If you unplug a cordless phone, you will need to make sure to remove the batteries from the handset to prevent the handset from transmitting.

Cell Phones and Tablets

Cell phones and tablets present a huge opportunity to reduce radio frequency impacts because there are so many services turned on by default, and most people don't even use many of them.

The biggest mistake most people make is thinking that turning their phone to airplane mode is enough to keep them safe. The problem is they aren't considering the other fields that are created when the device is plugged in and charging or running on battery.

The best low-EMF option for cell phones and tablets is to keep them completely powered off as much as possible. However, that isn't always possible, especially if you need to be reachable.

I recommend the following practices to keep your exposure to a minimum:

Keep devices powered off as much as possible. This is the safest option because the device is not transmitting radio frequency or creating a magnetic field or dirty electricity.

Charge the device as far away from you as possible. When your phone or tablet is plugged in, it creates magnetic, electric, and dirty electricity fields, so try to charge these at least six feet away from wherever you are.

Don't charge and use a device at the same time. If you charge and use these at the same time, not only are you exposing yourself to radio frequency, but also AC direct, AC magnetic, and dirty electricity.

Keep devices as far away from you as possible. Lots of people put their cell phones in their pockets or bras, or they use their laptops on their lap. Even if the phone is on standby, it still creates a magnetic field. Keep a device as far away as you can, even if it's just a few feet. And never use a laptop on your lap!

Disable settings you rarely use. Customizing certain device settings can make a huge difference in reducing the amount of radiation you're exposed to (plus, it extends your battery life). Here's what I recommend:

- Disable Wi-Fi.
- Disable Bluetooth.
- Disable GPS—I only turn this on if I need the maps functionality.
- Change automatic email delivery to "Manual" so email is only retrieved when the email application is launched.
- Enable the setting for more yellow light after dusk to reduce your blue light impact.
- For iPhone users only: Disable LTE (in Settings, Cellular).
- For iPhone users only: Disable Siri & Search (go into each application and disable for each one).

Use speakerphone. Instead of putting the phone next to your ear, use speakerphone unless you're in a car or elevator (otherwise the signal bounces around and increases).

Unplug the charging unit when it's not charging. The charging unit still conducts current when it's plugged in, so unplug it when it's done charging.

Don't keep these under the pillow or next to the bed. Even if these are not plugged in and on airplane mode, they still create a magnetic field that affects your sleep.

Buy an ethernet adapter. If you need to connect to the internet, adapters with an ethernet port on one end still allow you to get connected (this will not let you make calls, though).

Do Cell Phone Shields Work?

After reading about all the ways your cell phone is exposing you to EMF fields, it makes sense you want to protect yourself as much as you can. There are so many different cell phone shields, guards, and stickers that claim to shield you from EMF fields, though, that it can be confusing!

When you evaluate these products, look at what field or fields the product claims to shield against and the before and after measurements (by field type). Once you start looking for this information, you'll see that many of these products don't provide that information, which is a huge red flag.

The basic rule of thumb is if the phone can receive or make a call or a text message, there's a strong enough radio frequency signal for communication. It's also difficult to know how effective the shielding products are because each cell phone manufacturer is different, and the magnetic and radio frequency fields will vary between manufacturers.

Unless you have a meter for taking precise measurements, it's difficult to determine exactly what the reduction is.

Although these shields may help reduce the radiation, it's usually not enough to completely eliminate all of the fields.

Smart Homes and Security Systems

Security systems and smart homes can create issues because radio frequency is continuously transmitted at very high levels.

Smart homes have one large command center that transmits very high levels of radio frequency so it can communicate with all the devices such as lights, thermostats, cameras, and speakers throughout the house. To give you an idea of how much radiation is created, one single light switch on a wall can be over 18,000 microwatts per meter squared and transmit every twenty seconds.

Dismantling a smart home system is also very expensive in time and money because the switches are not traditional ones (remember, they have to transmit wirelessly) and additional work needs to be done to replace them with a traditional system.

Security systems do not have to be connected to an entire smart home system, but they can still have a central base station with remote satellite cameras that are plugged into an outlet and communicate wirelessly to the command center. Even if the central command center is hardwired into your modem, the satellites still transmit because they're looking for the signals from the command center, similar to a cordless phone communicating with the base station.

If your security system offers a non-wireless option for the satellites (be sure to check this in the technical specifications), you still need to go into the settings for each satellite and make sure wireless is not turned on. Otherwise it will be transmitting by default.

The safest option is for everything to be hardwired and to have wireless capability completely disabled.

Tips for security cameras: If you have wireless security cameras and only use them for specific occasions such as when you go on vacation, always try to have them installed on the outside of the house in places that won't impact you inside. For example, avoid having one installed next to a window where you spend a lot of time, or even a window that is a floor below that area.

Smart Appliances

Smart appliances are everyday household appliances like refrigerators, washing machines, or dryers with a radio frequency chip built into them. These chips can send out radio frequency and can often be controlled with smartphones or a smart home system.

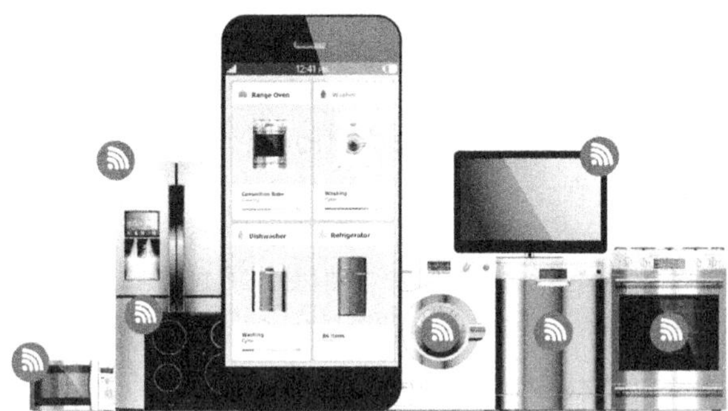

Some of the appliances allow you to completely disable wireless while others do not have that option. Each manufacturer is different, and the models offered by each manufacturer vary as well. This means that the responsibility is on the buyer to check and validate this before purchasing.

TVs and Cable Services

TVs are another household item that can create very high radiation levels, which can be challenging because all TVs have built-in wireless capability and not all TVs allow you to disable it.

That means it's your responsibility to check and validate that your TV allows you to turn off wireless before purchasing it.

Most TVs continue to transmit radio frequency when they're on standby (they're plugged in but not actively being used) unless wireless has been disabled.

When it comes to cable and content services, there are tons of options such as satellites, traditional cable, and internet services such as Roku, Fire Stick, and Apple TV—to name a few. Unfortunately, remote controls and plugins used with outlets or USB ports can create very high levels of radio frequency that transmit continuously. Even if the TV isn't actually being used, they can still transmit in standby mode.

The best way to ensure the TV and any other devices are not transmitting is to completely unplug them when they aren't in use.

Wireless Speakers

Wireless speakers have similar issues as cordless phones, internet boosters, and security systems. If they're plugged in and on standby, they can still transmit radio frequency continuously even if they're hardwired.

Although some wireless speakers allow you to disable wireless if Wi-Fi is turned on and you are connected to your network, the best way to ensure your wireless speaker isn't transmitting is to completely unplug it when it's not in use.

If your wireless speaker has a hardwired connection to your TV, make sure when the TV is turned on that it doesn't automatically enable wireless and start transmitting. I have seen this firsthand at a client's house. As soon as the TV turned on, the speaker powered on, overrode the wireless setting in the TV by enabling it, and started transmitting because it was looking for a music station. The only way to prevent this was by completely removing the speaker from the setup.

Internet Modems

Internet modems are one of the easiest things to remediate—but they're also where the most mistakes are made. That's because there are several steps to complete; otherwise, the modem will continue to transmit radio frequency throughout your house.

Modems continuously transmit radio frequency that easily goes through walls, windows, and doors, making them a challenge to mitigate.

If you have a router on your desk, you're getting the equivalent amount of radiation as you would from a cell antenna 100 feet or less away.[53, 54]

The safest and best option for internet connectivity is disabling all wireless on your modem and creating a hardwired ethernet connection.

Follow these steps to disable all radio frequency transmission:

Step 1: Log into your modem.

1. Open your internet browser on your computer.
2. Type in the IP address for your modem (if you don't know what this is, go online and enter your internet service provider and "how to log into modem," and it should return with instructions and an IP address).
3. You should be prompted to enter your username and password (usually on the bottom of your modem).

Step 2: Disable your personal hotspot.

*If you do not know if you have personal hotspot functionality or your ISP doesn't make this setting available, you may need to call them to verify and request them to disable if applicable.

1. Navigate to one of the settings tabs and disable this. (The exact location may vary depending on your internet service provider.)

Step 3: Disable both 2.4 GHz and 5 GHz Wi-Fi channels.

1. These are usually in the wireless settings.
2. Disable each channel; each channel usually appears in a separate tab, and you must disable each one separately.

Step 4: Check your work.

1. Make sure your settings have taken effect. You may need to completely power off your modem and then power back on to verify this.
2. Check that the wireless icon on the modem itself is not lit up.
3. If your modem has separate 2.4 and 5 GHz channels on the box, make sure that neither are lit up (ignore this step if your modem doesn't have these lights).
4. Check that the modem is not broadcasting by powering on a cell phone or computer, turning on wireless, and seeing if you can see your network.
5. Check that the personal hotspot is not broadcasting; this usually has a generic name like "xfinitywifi" or whatever your internet service provider's name is with "wifi" or something to that effect as part of the name.

Step 5: Hardwire your connection.

Once you've completed steps 1–5 and you've verified that your modem is not transmitting, you can hardwire your internet connection with an ethernet cord (I recommend using shielded cords).

Important: If you are a Windows user, be sure that airplane mode (on the main taskbar) is selected so that your laptop or CPU is not continuing to transmit. If you are a Mac user, you can disable this in the main Settings area.

Two common mistakes to look out for:

- Unintentionally disabling only one channel (not both)
- Not disabling the personal hotspot, which means radio frequency is transmitting at full power

If disabling all wireless in your modem is not an option for you, take the following steps to reduce your exposure (just be aware these won't totally eliminate EMF exposure):

1. Only plug in the modem when it's being used.
2. Completely unplug modem at night.
3. Reduce the power signal strength by logging into the modem and going into the wireless settings to reduce the signal strength (default is always set to 100%).

> **Note:** If the modem isn't completely unplugged and no steps have been taken to disable wireless, it is in standby mode and can still transmit radio frequency!

Boosters and Mesh Networks

Internet boosters and mesh network systems are very similar and should be avoided if possible because of the strength of radio frequency fields that are created.

Internet boosters extend wireless capability of the main modem for better wireless throughout the house. They transmit radio frequency around the clock just like a regular modem, and the strength of the field is very high, typically in the thousands of microwatts per meter squared. If you have purchased a modem, or you lease one from your internet service provider, these are typically offered as add-ons.

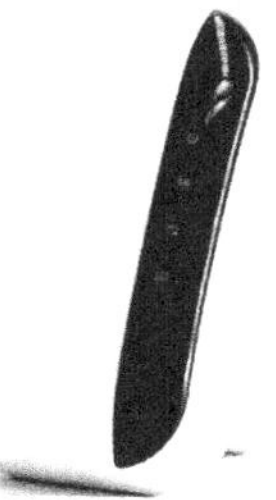

Mesh networks are complete third-party systems (e.g., you don't purchase them or lease through your internet service provider) that typically have a base station and then several satellite stations. The technology produces coverage that is similar to what you'd experience when you're walking through a hotel and don't lose your connection because the coverage "overlaps." These also transmit very high levels of radiation.

Don't make this DIYer mistake: Whether you have boosters or a mesh system, remember that if you disable or unplug the main modem or station, the satellites need to be unplugged as well. If they aren't unplugged, they continue to transmit radio frequency because they're looking for signals from the base component.

Do Router Guards Really Work?

The short answer is, it depends.

Shielding materials only shield up to a certain limit, and once that limit is reached, the shielding efficiency drops significantly, and radio frequency goes through the material.

Most router guards only shield against radio frequency and will not shield against magnetic fields or dirty electricity.

The only way to make sure that a router guard works is to have a good-quality meter and take measurements.

Internet over Power Lines

Internet over power lines (also known as broadband over power lines or BPL) is a non-wireless option that might seem like a great alternative to Wi-Fi but can create other issues.

Instead of having a wireless modem for internet connectivity, a central hub station is plugged into the wall, and smaller satellite plugins with ethernet adapters are plugged into outlets throughout the home to deliver your internet connectivity.

The problem is, these high radio frequencies are overlaid on top of the electricity that's circulating throughout the house (they're plugged into the 60 Hz outlets). This creates dirty electricity, which can make you feel worse or trigger EMF sensitivities.

Low-EMF Computers and Monitors

If you're wanting to find lower-EMF computers and monitors, you're in luck!

TCO is a Swedish nonprofit organization that certifies products based on sustainability criteria and includes electric and magnetic fields as part of this criteria. However, most manufacturers do not include TCO certification in their product description details. That means you need to find the products on the TCO site first and then find them online or in brick-and-mortar stores to get the details such as monitor size, adapter types, etc.

If you're willing to put in the extra legwork to find lower-radiation products, it's well worth it.

The process outlined below is the easiest and most efficient I've found for getting lower-EMF products:

1. Grab a pen and paper and create four columns on the paper: *Brand*, *Sales Name*, *Description*, and *Yes/No*. You will use this paper to keep track of the products you find on the TCO site.
2. Go to www.tcocertified.com.
3. Click on the Product Finder button on the main menu.

4. Select your search criteria (monitors, notebooks, etc.) or enter the brand name in the search box, whichever you prefer.
5. Filter the search results by date (newest released products first), and then start scrolling to find recent models.
6. The "Sales Name" column is what you'll use if you're searching online or if you walk into a store, so be sure to write down the sales name and brand on your sheet of paper.
7. Now you're going to go online, find the products, and get all the details such as size of the monitor (or laptop or other device), cost, etc. to decide if it's what you're looking for.
8. Write down your decision criteria in the Description column for each product that you're researching. You will use this to narrow down all the products and decide which one is the best for you. For any products you are not going to continue researching, write a "No" in the Yes/No column. Any final products you want to include in your final selection should have a "Yes" written in that column.

Wireless Printers

Wireless printers are one of the most overlooked EMF culprits in the home!

All printers today have wireless turned on by default, so unless you've manually gone into the settings and disabled wireless, you're most likely being impacted without even knowing it.

Printers can send out the same amount of radiation as a cordless phone or internet booster, travel the same distance, and create dirty electricity.

It's best to keep these completely unplugged when they're not being used.

Recap

Here's what you've learned in this section:

- ✓ The most common mistakes DIYers make when it comes to remediating sources inside the home
- ✓ Why you shouldn't go out and buy a bed canopy or install EMF paint without taking measurements first
- ✓ Why turning off the bedroom breaker switches can make things worse (and the correct approach to take)
- ✓ Baby monitor tips
- ✓ How personal care products can affect you
- ✓ How to use cell phones and tablets safely
- ✓ Smart homes and security system gotchas
- ✓ Smart appliances
- ✓ What to look for in TVs, cable services, and wireless speakers
- ✓ The right way to turn off wireless in your modem and disable transmission in your boosters
- ✓ How to find low-EMF computers and monitors
- ✓ How to use printers safely

PART 2

EMF SELF-CARE AND DETOXING

CHAPTER 6

HOW TO COMBAT EMFS WITH THE RIGHT NUTRITION

This chapter focuses on foods that help your body fight against radiation and the downstream health effects from EMF fields on your body. Most people are so focused on reducing their exposure to EMF fields that they overlook nutrition, but it's an important piece to completing the puzzle of fighting against EMF fields.

Since I'm not a nutritionist, I recommend working with a professional who can determine the best approach for you.

In the meantime, I have a special treat for you: the content of this section has been provided by Susie M. Earl, licensed Integrative Nutritionist and health food educator extraordinaire!

In this chapter you're going to learn about foods that will help you:

- Cleanse, detox, and purify from a general perspective
- Fight against radiation
- Boost your immune system
- Detox heavy metals

- Fight against cancer
- Counter the stress response
- Slow skin aging
- Support your cell membranes

Radiation and pollutants destroy or disrupt:

- Vitamins A, C, E, and K vitamins
- Essential fatty acids
- Calcium and neurohormones
- Central nervous system
- Cardiovascular system
- Endocrine system
- Immune system

In addition, brain chemistry is altered, particularly in the hypothalamus and cerebral cortex, which is the disruption in the blood-brain barrier. The cerebral cortex is like the bark on a tree wrapped around the brain to keep the brain protected. The hypothalamus directs a multitude of important functions—it wakes us up, gets our adrenaline flowing, and can make us feel exhilarated, angry, or unhappy, to name a few.

General Clean-Eating and Detoxing Principles

Before we get into the food, it's important to remember the essential role water and proper hydration play in keeping our body functioning smoothly.

- Stay hydrated with high-quality water throughout each day and after breaking the body's fast.
- Start with 6–8 ounces of water. You can add juice from a squeezed lemon, lime, or orange, which will liven up the flavor

and bring even more health benefits to the body. These citrus fruits have lots of vitamin C, a common benefit they share.

- Drink water often throughout the day to regulate hunger and craving symptoms. Hydration also helps keep the mind clear, alert, calm, and productive.
- If you want to change it up, other healthy options are coconut and aloe waters, which also come in a variety of fruit flavors.

General Clean-Eating Principles

As much as possible, eat clean, natural, fresh organic foods, and try to avoid the following:

- Processed foods
- White sugar
- Red meat
- Refined wheat
- Caffeine
- Homogenized milk

Elements that help cleanse, detoxify, purify, and heal many conditions are in rich chlorophyll-containing foods such as barley grass and chlorella.

Barley (wheat) grass contains all the nutrients required for life: vitamins, minerals, enzymes, and other proteins (amino acids), essential fatty acids, and chlorophyll. Chlorophyll closely resembles human blood and slows down bacterial growth. It detoxifies heavy metals from the body and helps with wound healing while detoxifying the liver and other organs. Chlorophyll also deodorizes the body, removing putrefactive bacteria from the colon, helps heal eleven types of skin diseases, relieves ulcers, gastritis, pancreatitis, and other inflammatory conditions, helps heal gum disease, and inhibits radiation and the metabolic activation of many carcinogens.

If the thought of eating grass or algae is less than appealing to you, there are pure chlorophyll supplements you can take instead.

Chlorella is a green freshwater microalgae that has even more chlorophyll than barley (wheat) grass, plus 55–65% protein with nineteen amino acids, including all the essential ones. Chlorella is also an excellent source of beta-carotene, vitamins B-1, B-2, B-3, B-6, B-12, pantothenic acid, folic acid, biotin, PABA, inositol, and vitamin C. Chlorella contains more B-12 than liver and contains essential minerals—iron, phosphorus, magnesium, calcium, zinc, potassium, sulfur, iodine, and trace amounts of manganese, sodium, and chlorophyll.

Teas That Support Your Body's General Well-Being

Special herbal teas and apple cider vinegar may support the human body's diet and overall well-being of the complete endocrine system as they detox the liver, kidneys, and lymphatic system such as:

- Pau d'arco herbal tea
- Black tea (containing tannin) with local raw honey
- Saffron (containing colchicine-lowering uric acid)
- Thyme tea

The Warburg Hypothesis claimed that the main compound in apple cider vinegar helps kill tumor cells. Scientist and Nobel Prize winner Otto Warburg believed that disease was primarily a nutritional problem and that it could not develop in people who ate a correct, natural diet. As a result, he claimed that 80% of cancer cases were avoidable. Warburg also suggested that a high level of acidity and low levels of oxygen in the body caused cancer. He based this hypothesis on the fact that cancer cells produce acid as they grow, even in environments that are not usually acidic.[55]

What we know for sure is that apple cider vinegar and other types of vinegar appear to be good sources of antioxidants, which will help:

- Keep the body healthy

- Fight off free radicals that damage cells
- Balance blood sugar
- Protect against bacteria
- Promote healthy weight loss (with eating a low-calorie diet)
- Raise HDL, the good cholesterol, and lower levels overall

Immune System Boosters

There are several foods you can add into your diet (if you haven't already) that will better support your immune system.

These fruits and vegetables support your immune system and contain natural vitamin A:

- Lima beans
- Potatoes
- Yams
- Sweet potatoes
- Asparagus
- Tomatoes
- Onions
- Spinach
- Mangos
- Grapes
- Avocados
- Pears
- Oranges (plus peel and pulp)
- Apples (plus seeds and skin)
- Strawberries

The following un-sprouted seeds help to increase blood platelets. This is essential for fighting infection and boosting the immune system.

- Sunflower
- Sesame* [(raw and ground, also called tahini, contains a substance called Complex T and essential fatty acids (EFAs)]
- Pumpkin
- Almonds
- Cashews

Many essential fatty acids, such as GLA and EPA, are vital for proper functioning of the immune system and protecting against cancer. These can be found in:

- Flaxseed oil
- Evening primrose oil
- Certain fish, particularly salmon and foods high in omega-3 fatty acids

Coenzyme Q10 offers immense benefits to the immune system and aids in retarding the aging process while helping to manage high blood pressure, angina, and obesity symptoms.

Zinc helps strengthen the T-cell-producing thymus gland as well as support the immune system in fighting off colds and viruses; the recommended amount is no more than 50–100 mg daily. Moreover, it is available in grains, nuts, seeds, legumes, turkey, pork, and shellfish (especially oysters).

Foods That Fight Radiation[56]

There are a number of foods that can help your body fight against radiation.

Miso (made from naturally fermented soybeans), rice, and barley are among the best. Miso is a superior source of good whole protein and aids digestion; it's low in fats and helps neutralize environmental pollution including radiation.

Fermented (lactic acid) vegetables and juices contain medicinal properties and can help with biological treatment of many conditions, including cancer, arthritis, multiple sclerosis, kidney and liver diseases, and digestive disorders.

Good sources of fermented foods high in lactic acid include:

- Sauerkraut
- Beets
- Carrots
- Green and red pepper
- Beet tops
- Swiss chard
- Celery

Examples of cultured (fermented) milk products are:

- Yogurt
- Kefir
- Buttermilk
- Unprocessed cheese products also contain friendly bacteria, such as Lactobacillus acidophilus and other strains that perform valuable duties in your colon and synthesize germ-destroying antibodies in your colon.

Anti-Radiation

Cruciferous vegetables contain substances that inhibit breast and colon cancer growth and contain dithiolthiones (a type of cancer chemopreventive agent), a nontoxic group of compounds that have antioxidant, anticancer, and anti-radiation properties.

Sources include:

- Broccoli
- Spinach
- Kale
- Swiss chard
- Romaine
- Endive
- Chicory
- Escarole
- Watercress
- Collard
- Mustard
- Dandelion greens
- Carrots
- Sweet potatoes
- Yams
- Pumpkins
- Winter squash
- Cantaloupe
- Apricots
- Peaches
- Papaya
- Watermelon

Bee and flower pollens contain a special brand of magic. They are excellent healing foods containing all essential amino acids, vitamins A, D, E, K, C, bioflavonoids, B-complex (especially pantothenic acid and B-3), and 27 minerals. Bee pollen is beneficial in treating anemia, chronic prostatitis, constipation, flatulence, and colon infections, especially diarrhea.

The best way to add this sweet healthy treat is to substitute your daily sugars with honey. Local farm raised is the most beneficial for our bio-individual needs and helps with seasonal allergies. Stir one or two tablespoons in warm water or in your favorite warm beverage. Or add it to a nut butter on toasted bread for a great treat.

The University of Vienna's Women's Clinic conducted a study involving twenty-five women with inoperative uterine cancer, all of whom received radiotherapy. The fifteen who took twenty grams of bee pollen three times a day tolerated the radiation much better than the ten who did not.

Epidemiological data suggest that a high-fiber diet protects against large bowel cancer perhaps for several reasons. It dilutes bowel carcinogens, decreases colon transit time, and changes the composition and metabolic activity of the fecal flora and certain carcinogenic substances in the colon.

This is why it's healthier to eat whole grains containing the bran and the fiber, as well as whole fruits and vegetables, instead of their processed, partitioned counterparts.

Examples of high-fiber foods include:

- Whole grains like barley, bran flakes, quinoa, and brown rice
- Fruits like raspberries, pears, apple with skin, banana, oranges, and strawberries
- Vegetables like peas, broccoli, turnip greens, and Brussels sprouts

Foods That Help Prevent Cancer

Calcium and magnesium are protective supplements and minerals found in our whole foods and also easily consumed in capsules, tablets, or liquid drops. The *New England Journal of Medicine* reported that calcium might prevent precancerous cells from becoming cancerous while protecting against strontium-90 and other radioisotopes. Plus, both calcium and magnesium reduce the risk of osteoporosis by supporting bone health early in life.

Leading sources of calcium include:

- Low-fat plain yogurt and Part-skim ricotta cheese
- Sardines
- Salmon
- Fat-free milk
- Swiss cheese and Cheddar cheese
- Teff
- Turnip greens
- White beans
- Greens
- Filberts and almonds

Magnesium-rich foods include:

- Quinoa and Wild rice
- Sunflower seed kernels
- Avocado
- Halibut
- Tofu
- Amaranth
- Greens
- All unrefined whole grains

Selenium, along with vitamins C and E, fight against cancers and protect against carcinogens by helping to produce a free-radical scavenger called glutathione peroxidase.

Good sources of selenium include:

- Brazil nuts
- Grape seed extract
- Flounder
- Shrimp
- Turkey
- Chicken breast

DHEA is the most dominant hormone in the body. DHEA is thought to be the "Fountain of Youth" hormone because it can help extend life span.

DHEA helps to:

- Counteract the adverse effects of stress
- Boost the immune system
- Regulate blood cholesterol
- Lower blood pressure

DHEA does not come from foods, but wild yams contain a substance similar to DHEA that is used to make DHEA in the laboratory. The body manufactures DHEA naturally in the adrenal glands.[57]

Countering the Stress Response

By now you know that EMF fields trigger the stress response in your body. When this happens, it also affects your body's ability to process and absorb proteins. To counter this, your body needs to be replenished with protein so it can create other essential sub-proteins.

This can include any variety of proteins such as:

- Animals (beef, chicken, turkey)
- Fish
- Nuts and seeds
- Whole grains and vegetables

Your body will make better use of the proteins—and be better able to detox heavy metals from your system—when it is processing in a calm, low-stress environment.

Heavy Metals Detox

Pacific kelp is used to bind and detoxify heavy metals from the body (lead, mercury, cadmium, and agar). Sea vegetables and other kelp products contain sodium alginate, a non-nutritious extract.

Agar is a thickening agent used instead of gelatin or cornstarch. Kelp and dulse are excellent sources of iodine. Both are great in protecting against radioactive iodine treatments, which gradually shrink your thyroid and ultimately destroy the gland.

High iodine foods include:

- Seafood
- Beef liver
- Pineapple
- Eggs
- Whole wheat
- Seaweeds

When the body has an adequate supply of organic iodine, radioiodine is not readily absorbed by the thyroid or the ovaries.

Membrane Support

Vitamin E neutralizes harmful free radicals and protects delicate membranes.

Natural sources include:

- Kale
- Sweet potato
- Wheat germ
- Almonds
- Hazelnuts
- Sunflower seeds
- Blueberries

When choosing a supplement, look for "natural" vitamin E, preferably a brand containing some "mixed tocopherols," which contain various amounts of three tocopherols. And try to avoid synthetic vitamin E (often denoted dl-alpha-tocopherol), which may include forms foreign to the body and poorly utilized by the body.

Keeping Your Youthful Glow

EMF fields make your skin age faster than normal. Yikes! To help counter this, consume vitamins A, C, beta-carotene, and carotenoids (which convert into vitamin A). These manufacture antibodies, maintain and protect mucous membranes, and support the immune system, thymus gland, and master gland. They help guard against tumor formation and cancer and help reverse the aging process of the skin caused by ultraviolet light. Lycopene, the carotenoid prominent in tomatoes, also appears to protect against certain cancers.

Leading sources of vitamin A include:

- Organ meats
- Fish
- Egg yolks
- Sweet potato
- Pumpkin puree
- Kale
- Spinach (dark-green vegetables)
- Red and orange peppers
- Tomato juice
- Carrots
- Watermelon
- Cantaloupe
- Apricots

Vitamin C sources include:

- Red and green peppers
- Broccoli
- Brussels sprouts
- Black currants
- Grapefruit
- Orange juice

Vitamin C, also called ascorbic acid due to its antiscorbutic properties, can counteract toxins and radiation. A protective dose is 500–2,000 mg. If you consume five servings of fruits and vegetables high in vitamin C every day, you'll have no trouble meeting this recommendation.

Nutrition and Healthy Sleep Hygiene

It's important to acknowledge the importance of sleep because EMF fields can significantly impact the quality of sleep you are able to get every night and can prevent you from getting the deep sleep cycles that your body needs to heal and repair itself.

Positive health impacts to your body may start with the quantity and quality of rest, which equals better brain power, cardiovascular strength, and gut health. Good sleep enables the body to use vitamins more efficiently.

The lack of proper rest gradually lowers resistance to illnesses such as colds and flu and eventually blocks the body's ability to naturally heal itself. Lack of quality sleep also means you're more susceptible to more serious health issues like cancer and other lifestyle-limiting illnesses.

A note about melatonin: This cancer-inhibiting hormone secreted by the pineal gland affects the sleep cycle, fertility, and the immune system. If you feel you would benefit from melatonin, be sure to select a high-quality natural supplement. Quality rest and relaxation of mind and body are necessary for the human body to grow, regenerate, and continue to thrive. [58]

Recap

Here's what you've learned in this section:

- ✓ General detox and clean-eating principles
- ✓ Why you need to stay hydrated
- ✓ Foods that fight radiation
- ✓ Food that help fight cancer
- ✓ Foods that detox metals from your system
- ✓ Foods that support healthy membranes
- ✓ Foods that help prevent your skin from aging
- ✓ The importance of quality sleep

CHAPTER 7

HOLISTIC SOLUTIONS GOOD FOR THE HEART AND SOUL

As you've learned, EMF fields literally create toxins in your body, which means you need a routine to remove those toxins. I consider this element to be just as important as reducing your exposure to EMF fields because without it, the toxins continue to accumulate in your body. Most people don't think of EMF fields as a toxin, so they don't treat them accordingly. This means they are missing a crucial component of managing their exposure.

This is one of my favorite parts of managing my EMF exposure. I enjoy many of these practices as a treat to myself, so it was even better once I learned about their ability to combat effects of EMF fields. There are so many different options, so it's nice to be able to choose the practice that feels best for your body in the moment.

The goal of this section is to give you a basic framework of natural holistic solutions that help offset the damages from EMFs. From there, you can modify these techniques and create practices that work for you.

I also want to stress and recommend checking in with your healthcare professional or a specialist in the following disciplines to make sure whatever you choose will be a good fit. Most likely you'll also find that several practitioners combine modalities, which can provide even greater benefits.

Soaks, Scrubs, and Massages

Foot soaks, salt scrubs, and massages are some of my go-to favorites when I don't have a lot of time. These are easy fixes!

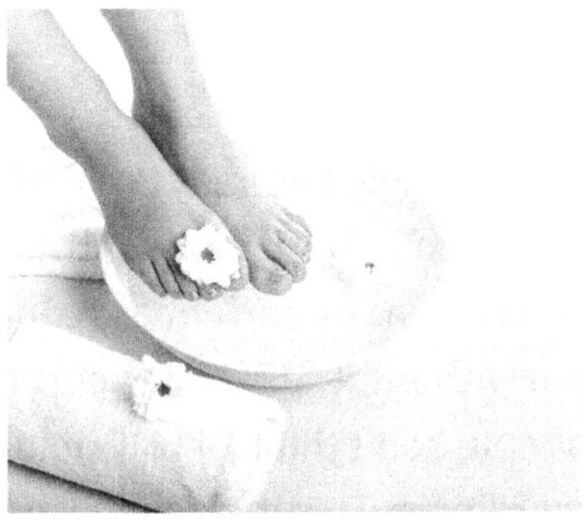

Soaking your feet in bentonite clay or salt is great for pulling toxins from your feet.

Follow these instructions for an Epsom salt and clay foot soak:

1. You'll need a tub of water big enough to put your feet in.
2. Get a comfortable chair to sit in.
3. Measure ½ cup of Epsom salts or 3–4 tablespoons of bentonite clay.
4. Heat some water, enough to fully cover your feet, as hot as you can stand it.
5. Add the Epsom salts or the clay to the water.
6. Place your feet in the water.
7. Sit back and relax! (This is also a good time to meditate.)

Note: Alternatively, you can mix 1–2 tablespoons of clay with 1 tablespoon of apple cider vinegar (which is antibacterial) to create a muddy paste and apply to the bottoms of your feet feet for 15–20 minutes and then wash and rinse away.

A salt scrub is my go-to when I'm super tired after a long day and want to go straight to bed. If I'm feeling a little wired or I've been around a lot of EMF fields and feel "buzzy," I opt for a steaming hot shower or bath with the water as hot as I can stand it and a good salt scrub. And then I crash for the evening. ☺

Salt is loaded with negative ions, so it helps get rid of the positive charges your skin is holding. From an energetic perspective, salt also helps clear and flush out your energy field, so if you're sensitive to energy like I am, this will help get rid of that "energetic sludge" you've picked up throughout the day.

If you don't have a salt scrub, add some Epsom salts to a small bowl with just enough water to get the salt wet (but not diluted) and use that as your scrub.

Lastly, don't forget to drink lots of water after any detoxing. Keep yourself well hydrated so those toxins can flush out of your body.

Massage is my method of choice when I want to kick back, relax, and not have to think, but it does take some planning to find a good practitioner and schedule the appointment in advance. Massage is great for draining those toxins from your lymph nodes and getting your body out of that fight-or-flight mode triggered by EMF fields.

I recommend finding a practitioner who specializes in lymph nodes, but if you have trouble finding one, ask your practitioner to focus on the following areas:

- The back of your neck, toward the base of the neck
- The lymph node areas below the ears and jawline
- Areas where you feel EMF sensitivities
- The top of the head or crown chakra

Emu oil used in massage is very beneficial, as it's full of good omega 3, 6, and 9 and vitamin A. The oil soaks in through the skin, the largest organ, and is known to aid in reducing inflammation, arthritis, and skin damage associated with cancer radiation.

Saunas

Saunas are a great solution to literally steam those toxins out of your body! However, saunas can present unique challenges when it comes to EMF fields, including the infrared saunas.

There are pros and cons for the different types of saunas available, which creates challenges when you're trying to find a low-EMF product.

Traditional saunas that are in a separate enclosed building or a custom sauna room in a house with a single heater unit tend to have lower EMF fields than the smaller portable units.

One of the challenges with the portable units is that there are heaters on the sides and usually behind the torso and the back of the legs. While they may have low magnetic fields, once they're turned on, the AC direct fields can increase to as much as 400 V/m, depending on the wiring, electrical current, and number of heaters.

If you are looking at purchasing a sauna, I recommend purchasing a meter for both AC magnetic and direct fields. Measure inside the sauna in different spots when the sauna is simply plugged in versus when it is turned on.

If you are sensitive to EMF fields, I recommend experimenting with a few different saunas and monitoring how you feel after a sauna to help determine if this is a solution that will benefit you.

Essential Oils

Essential oils are another natural solution that can help fight against EMF fields. These are pure extracts from herbs, flowers, and trees and are extremely potent, so they're often used with a carrier oil such as jojoba, vitamin E, or fractionated coconut oil. These carrier oils dilute the oil without hindering its effectiveness.

You can purchase glass bottles of various sizes, ranging from 5 mL to several ounces, to store the essential oil and carrier oil mixture. Some of the bottles have rollerball inserts so you can roll the finished product onto your skin. Normal caps are available too.

One of the things I like about essential oils is they also work at a subconscious level and can help shed light on and release unconscious thoughts or patterns we are holding in our bodies that can manifest as pain or disease. I highly recommend finding a practitioner who specializes in this knowledge.

You might consider starting with a class of oils called sesquiterpenes that support brain health. The following oils are included in this class of oils:

- Cedarwood
- Copaiba
- Vetiver
- Sandalwood
- Patchouli
- Ginger
- Myrrh
- Spikenard
- Black pepper
- Ylang ylang
- Helichrysum
- Melissa

You should also ask your essential oils practitioner to recommend oils that will help with other areas affected by EMFs, such as your immune system and inflammation, to name a few.

I apply the oils in a few different areas:

- At the base of my neck in the back
- Under the jaw near the lymph nodes
- My heart chakra

Some oils can be applied to specific locations for maximum benefit. You'll also find there's a specific ratio of drops to carrier oil for maximum effectiveness. Again, consult your essential oils practitioner for specifics.

I typically recommend purchasing essential oils from a practitioner instead of from a drugstore. This is the best way to ensure your oils are pure and of high quality.

Meditation

As you know by now, EMF fields trigger your brain into a hyperactive state and kick off the stress response in your body. I use meditation as often as I can to help counter these effects.

What's great about meditation is the wide range of options for getting into a relaxed state of mind. Also, it's free, and you can do this just about anywhere.

One of the other things I like is that it's really easy to combine this technique with another remedy, like meditating after a salt scrub or foot soak.

If you're new to meditation, you might start out with a guided meditation, which will walk you through the process of relaxing and getting centered.

One of the things I do to get relaxed and centered is to focus on my breathing because it gives my brain something to do and keeps my thoughts from wandering. If it's nighttime and I don't want to close my eyes and risk falling asleep, I'll light a candle and focus on the candle as I'm counting and doing my breathing exercises.

Here are the steps that I take:

1. Pick a number that represents the number of seconds you will inhale, exhale, and hold your breath for (let's use four as an example).
2. Get into a relaxed sitting position and close your eyes.
3. Breathe in slowly for four seconds, letting your lungs expand on the inhale.
4. Keeping your lungs expanded and holding your breath, count for four more seconds (don't continue to breathe in).
5. Exhale slowly, counting to four seconds.
6. Keeping your lungs emptied and holding your breath, count for four more seconds (don't continue to breathe out).
7. Repeat steps 2–6 as many times as feels right for you. If four seconds feels too short or too long, increase or decrease the number of seconds that you hold your breath.

Note: Mala beads are an easy way to keep track of the number of breath cycles you complete, and you can get them in many shapes, sizes, and materials. Mine are amethyst beads that are about eight millimeters in diameter, so they're not too big and bulky when I'm holding them.

Tibetan and Crystal Sound Bowls

Sound therapy is my go-to practice when I need to seriously hit the reset button on my body.

As you learned earlier in this book, our bodies resonate with and respond to EMF fields, which gets them all out of whack. On the flip side, our bodies also resonate to healing tones and frequencies!

Tibetan sound bowls are metal bowls of different sizes. They are usually made from copper, tin, zinc, iron, silver, gold, and nickel and are tuned to specific frequencies and chakras. A sound bowl practitioner plays the bowls by rubbing the rim with a leather-wrapped or wooden mallet.

A sound bowl that's tuned for your solar plexus (usually one of the larger bowls) is placed on your stomach while you're lying on a massage table, and the sound bowl practitioner will "play" the bowl, allowing the vibrations and frequencies to reset your body to its natural frequency. The process is repeated, using different bowls attuned to other areas of the body.

The techniques vary by practitioner; for example, some will play the bowls on both your front and back, and some will have you stand in a bowl.

What's a Sound Bath?

A sound bath is a group sound therapy session where a sound bowl practitioner plays a set of bowls for a duration of time—say, 60–90 minutes. Participants come in and lie down on yoga mats for the duration of the sound bath. Oftentimes, there is more than one sound practitioner or different types of bowls and gongs. Some sound baths also incorporate guided meditations.

Other types of sound therapies:

- Crystal bowls—there are clear crystal quartz bowls and bowls made from gemstones such as rose quartz
- Gongs (also one of my favorites!)
- Tuning forks

Acupuncture and Yoga

Strengthening your personal energy field is another way to help your body fight EMF fields. This can take some time to build up (e.g., it's not going to happen overnight), but it definitely helps.

While this doesn't cure you from being affected or triggered by EMF fields, it can decrease your sensitivity to EMF fields and triggers. When I started kundalini yoga, it took about six to eight weeks of weekly classes to feel a noticeable difference because the changes were so subtle and gradual.

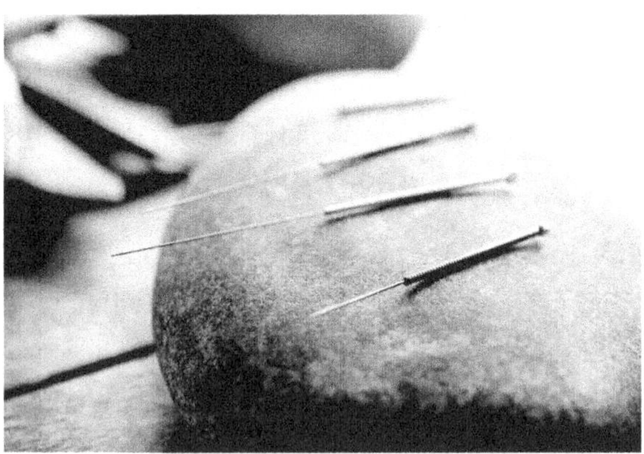

Other practices that can help strengthen your field:

- Acupuncture
- Yoga
- Tai chi
- Qi gong

Acupuncture is a holistic solution I didn't take to immediately. To be honest, I really had to work at being able to enjoy it. I had a completely unfounded fear of needles that goes back to my childhood, when I was chased around the house to get my shots. Childhood memories aside, acupuncture is a gentle, easy way to strengthen your energy field and detox at the same time.

And while you're lying there relaxing, it's also a great time to get in a little meditation for some added benefits!

Yoga, tai chi, and qi gong (to name just a few) are centuries-old practices that help to strengthen your energy field. One of the things I like about these is once you've mastered the moves, you can do them on the go or when you're traveling if you can't get to your studio or class.

Earthing

If you're looking for a simple, easy solution to help balance your personal field and combat feeling "buzzy" from EMFs, then earthing may be a good solution for you.

Earthing is the simple act of taking off your shoes and socks and planting your bare feet on the earth.

Here's how this works:

1. Our electronic devices, synthetic fabrics, products, and materials produce positively charged ions, and our environment ends up being "overly charged."
2. Earth, on the other hand, is naturally overloaded with negatively charged ions!
3. An imbalance occurs because we end up absorbing and "holding" these positively charged ions on our skin (and synthetic materials).
4. When we take off our shoes and socks and stand on the bare earth, our field automatically neutralizes and balances itself out. Pretty cool, huh?

The amount of time needed to balance your field may vary depending on your sensitivities. I recommend at least twenty minutes and up to an hour and a half, depending on your symptoms. From my personal experience, a "normal" grounding time is about thirty minutes. If I've been around a lot of Wi-Fi and can really feel the effects, then it takes longer, sometimes an hour and a half.

Tip: If you don't have dirt or grass to plant your bare feet on, you can use cement because cement will conduct current, though asphalt does not.

What About Earthing Products?

Earthing products such as earthing pads, mats, blankets, or sheets have a grounding rod that connects the product to the earth or a cord that plugs into an outlet.

These products act as the middleman so you don't have to take off your shoes and socks and stand on the grass. Use caution with these products because, even though they are technically grounded, you're still touching them and they are conductive. This often results in symptoms or EMF triggers.

A few precautions with earthing and earthing products:

- If you do natural earthing, you need to be aware of ground harmonics from power poles, power lines, and houses grounded to the earth in close proximity.
- Using the synthetic earthing products, you need to remember that the product is conductive and you're attracting fields to that conductive material that you're attached to. If you have high levels of EMF fields, they may cause you to feel worse because those fields will be attracted to the conductive product like a magnet, and the increase of those fields can make you feel worse.
- If you have a synthetic earthing product and ground directly to an outlet, keep in mind that electrical surges are a normal part of the electricity delivery to your home. Being attached to the earthing product, you also receive those electrical surges and can feel worse as a result.

If you plan to try earthing, I recommend going the all-natural route far away from utility poles or power lines so you get minimal ground harmonics. Find a nice sunny lawn or beach, take off your shoes and socks, plant your feet on the ground, and sit back and enjoy the benefits!

Crystals and Salt Lamps

Do crystals or salt lamps help combat EMFs?

I get this question all the time!

They do help, but probably not in the way you think.

When I get this question, I always think back to an anonymous quote I saw years ago, "We're all just a bunch of jiggling parts." It totally applies when you're working with crystals.

You may recall from earlier that humans have our own frequency that we vibrate at. And crystals have their own frequencies as well. Because everything has its own vibration, right?

The practice of using crystals for healing purposes goes back thousands of years, and there are a number of crystals known for helping to protect against EMF fields.

How we react to crystals is subjective and totally different for each person. A person's unique vibration and the crystal's vibration also play an important role.

Consider the following list of crystals known to fight against EMFs:

- **Shungite** is one I use as an all-around toxin remover, and I store it on a selenite slab. This is the most powerful one I've found for recuperating from EMFs. Not everyone is drawn to it, though, so test it first to make sure it feels right for you.
- **Black tourmaline** is a general negative energy fighter; I use this in combination with shungite when I feel the EMF fields are really high or if I feel like I'm starting to get EMF symptoms.
- **Jet** is another good toxin remover, and it's a little more gentle than shungite.
- **Brown tourmaline (dravite)** is very grounding, it's known to calm the nervous system.
- **Selenite** is a good choice if you are triggered by EMFs, and I use this with shungite because it's a gentle detoxer.

- **Amazonite** is one I'm still experimenting with, but it strengthens your personal field to help transmute EMF fields.
- **Sodalite** helps strengthen your field when you're holding the stones. I actually have an amazing sodalite necklace that I wear when I'm out and know that I'm going to be exposed to a lot of radio frequency.
- **Kyanite** is one I use when I feel like I have a lot of brain fog from being exposed to radio frequency; it helps clear this up.
- **Pyrite** is great for fighting EMF fields in general.
- **Green aventurine** helps quite a bit with the lower frequencies like ground harmonics and helps you feel more grounded.

When it comes to selecting crystals, the rule of thumb I follow and recommend is to go with the stone that resonates with you, one you feel pulled toward—whether it makes logical sense or not. If a certain stone doesn't "feel" right or just doesn't produce any feeling, I listen to my intuition and put it down and move on.

Below are some of my favorite combinations I've used over the years and continue to use to this day. Use these as a starting guideline, but discover and refine what works best for you, incorporating the stones that you're pulled toward.

You can use these when you're just sitting and relaxing, or you can give it some intention and hold them during meditation. I've also been known to bring in a few crystals for sound therapy as well or to sleep with them under my pillow. ☺

Selenite, Shungite, and Jet

This was my favorite combination when I first became sensitive to EMF fields and needed a solution that was strong enough to detox but gentle enough that it didn't cause any other reactions.

What you need:

- Palm-size peach selenite
- High-quality brown tourmaline
- Black jet

What to do:

- Hold the selenite in one hand (I use my left because it's the receiving side).
- Hold the black jet and brown tourmaline in your right hand to pull out the toxins and negative energies.

Selenite + Shungite

These two stones are the ones I reach for if I feel like I've been triggered or like I'm about to have a reaction from being exposed to EMF fields.

What you need:

- Selenite wand or sphere (I usually like the square wands that are about a quarter-inch wide, but use whatever feels right for you)
- Shungite

What to do:

- Hold the selenite in one hand and the shungite in another.
- If I feel like I've been triggered by EMF fields, I'll take the selenite wand and point it at the area that is hurting and move the wand along that area.

Sodalite and Kyanite

I go with this combination if I've had a full day and feel like my head needs to be cleared.

What you need:

- Sodalite stones
- Two pieces of blue kyanite that you can easily hold in each hand

What to do:

- Hold one piece of kyanite and sodalite in each hand.
- Take several deep breaths, closing your eyes if it helps. I usually feel sensations in my head as things start to clear. I also sometimes feel it in my heart chakra area or my hands as I'm holding them.

A few considerations if you're new to crystals:

- Avoid keeping them in direct sunlight for more than an hour.
- They can "absorb" energies, so be sure to clean them! I always keep them energetically clean by setting them on clear slabs of selenite and burning sage or incense and passing the crystal through the smoke. (You can find lots of great books that will tell you different ways to clean crystals.)
- Always go with your intuition when picking out a crystal or deciding if it's completed its work (e.g., maybe the crystal doesn't feel right anymore or doesn't seem to help as much as when you started working with it).
- Some crystals should not be exposed to water; for example, selenite will start to dissolve.

Do Salt Lamps Really Work?

Back in the earthing section you learned that our field gets overly charged with positive ions from our electronics and that the earth is loaded with negative ions, which helps restore balance to the body.

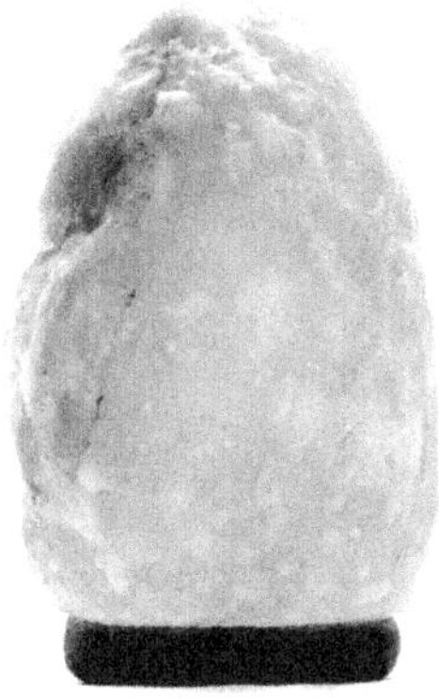

I have great news for you: salt is also loaded with negative ions!

It would seem to make sense to add a few salt lamps to your room and bingo! Your room is now free of EMF fields.

Unfortunately, it doesn't work quite like that.

Salt lamps *do* help balance out the positive-to-negative-ion ratio in the air, but they don't actually do anything to the EMF fields themselves. In addition, if a salt lamp has a cord or wire attached and is plugged in, you're creating an AC direct field and an AC magnetic field.

If you love the vibe of the salt lamps, you can still easily make them low-EMF. Either buy the candle-lamps that hold a votive, or, if you have an existing lamp, remove the bulb and cord and insert a votive. Voila!

Recap

Here's what you've learned in this section:

- ✓ How foot soaks, salt scrubs, and massage help detox your body
- ✓ Recommendations when it comes to saunas, AC direct fields, and monitoring any symptoms
- ✓ Essential oils that can help support healthy brain function
- ✓ How meditation helps counter the fight-or-flight response triggered by EMFs
- ✓ How sound therapy can help "reset" your body to its natural vibration
- ✓ How strengthening your personal field can help fight against EMF fields
- ✓ What earthing is and how it can be beneficial
- ✓ How crystals and salt lamps can help you with EMFs

CHAPTER 8

PREVENTIVE PRACTICES FOR THE REAL WORLD

Minimizing your risk and exposure from EMF fields means managing your home environment AND knowing what to do when you're out in the world.

One of the mistakes people make is minimizing EMF fields in their home and thinking they're "good." That isn't enough.

When my sensitivities started disappearing, I was able to get back out in the world again.

One sunny day, I was having lunch at one of my favorite restaurants with one of my best friends in an open-air atrium. I was thrilled to finally be out again. There weren't any cell towers or antennas in plain sight or in close proximity, and I knew I was in a fairly protected area.

Later that night, I ended up with an EMF reaction. I wondered how this could have happened and where the sources were, since I'd done my homework and looked for nearby towers beforehand. The culprits? Cell antennas high up in the rafters, directly above where we were sitting and painted the exact same color as the roof so they were pretty much invisible to the naked eye.

That's when I realized I needed to have a solid process and checklist of what to look for when I'm not at home. Since I got into the habit, it's become part of my normal routine, and I hardly ever get EMF reactions anymore.

This is what happens if you only clear EMFs from your home environment and forgo everything else:

1. You'll miss lots of easy opportunities to reduce EMF exposure without a technology plan.
2. You're at risk of developing permanent EMF sensitivities if you don't know what EMF symptoms to look out for.
3. You'll get triggered when you leave your house because you don't know how to prevent triggers.
4. You'll experience longer recuperation times because you haven't created a recuperation plan.
5. You'll get sick or triggered by EMFs when traveling.

Prevent EMF Triggers When You're Not at Home

One of the biggest challenges everyone has, whether they're sensitive to EMF fields or not, is knowing what to look for and avoid when they're out of the house.

If you're sensitive to EMFs, it can be especially frustrating because it's almost like you have to expect to get triggered when you go outside, and it shouldn't have to be that way.

Below are EMF life hacks that I've refined over the years. These have helped me get my social life back to normal:

Step 1: Research where you're going to be.

1. Search on Antennasearch beforehand to see if there are any antennas on the building or nearby cell towers.
2. Look up at the roof of the building before you walk in and see if there are antennas mounted on it or along the top floor. Since Antennasearch isn't 100% correct every time, I always check this just to make sure.

3. Look at the buildings next door (if there are any) to see if they have antennas mounted on them that might impact you.

Step 2: Once you're inside, check for sources outside coming in.

You'll want to take a look at where things are outside that might be coming in so you can find the places you don't want to be near (if possible). This can be fields coming in through windows or fields coming at you if you're sitting beside an external wall. If you're sitting outside, it's even more important to take a look around you because there aren't any walls to help protect you.

- ❑ Utility poles
- ❑ Overhead power lines and number of disks (silver ones indicating more current)
- ❑ Transformer buckets (size and quantity)
- ❑ Small cells (on poles or overhead power lines)
- ❑ Utility service drop (large boxes)
- ❑ Smart meters and direction they're pointing

Step 3: Look for sources inside.

Now that you've identified all of the sources outside coming in, you'll want to note everything inside so you're not sitting right underneath or right next to some of the following items:

- ❑ Security cameras and sensors
- ❑ Wireless access points
- ❑ Lighting systems (e.g., fluorescents, LEDs, etc.)
- ❑ Light switches and dimmers
- ❑ Cordless phones
- ❑ iPad or other tablet registers

Step 4: Minimize your impact.

Once you've assessed the situation and know what your impact is, you can decide whether you're good to stay or simply need to leave and find a place that's better for you.

Recognize and Manage EMF Symptoms

Recognizing and managing EMF symptoms is important because sensitivity to EMF fields never completely goes away. You can significantly reduce your triggers so you rarely have them, but you will most likely always be able to feel EMF fields even if they don't trigger you.

People usually only find out after the fact that they are sensitive to EMFs, and by that point they've wasted time and money and have gone through several doctors and physicians trying to narrow down what's wrong with them.

The first step is knowing what the common symptoms are so you'll recognize them if they show up in your life (if they haven't already). The second step is tracking symptoms so you can determine which fields you're sensitive to and how your body feels. From there you can prevent further symptom development.

If you believe you are sensitive to EMFs, you should start working with your healthcare professional to address them.

> Weaker immune systems are more susceptible to EMF sensitivities, and even if you don't experience symptoms, the biological impacts are still occurring in the body.

Below is a list of common symptoms people can experience as they start developing EMF sensitivities:

- Poor sleep (not sleeping through the night, trouble falling asleep, restlessness)

- Headaches, migraines, pressure headaches
- Tinnitus (high-pitched ringing in the ears) or pain in the inner ear
- Tightness in the jaw or jaw pain
- Feeling "wired" or anxious, especially in the morning when waking up
- Hyperactivity, especially in children who are sensitive and have ADHD, autism, or behaviors along the spectrum
- Dizziness or lightheadedness
- Tingling sensations or pain when using cell phones, laptops, or other devices that are enabled with Wi-Fi or Bluetooth
- Fatigue and exhaustion
- Nausea
- Vertigo
- Exacerbated sensitivities such as allergies or asthma

Below are steps you can take to start tracking your symptoms to help prevent triggers, identify which fields you're sensitive to, and reduce your recovery time.

Step 1: Start tracking your symptoms.

You can do this in a small journal you carry with you or a notes app on your cell phone. The goal is to have something on hand that allows you to make a few simple notes immediately and not forget about it.

Write down the date (important!), where you went, how much time you spent there, and detailed notes about your symptoms. That makes it easy to go back and recognize common symptoms to look out for.

Step 2: Track when and where your symptoms are triggered.

Start identifying what places and devices trigger you and how long it takes for your symptoms to start. Sometimes it's immediate, and sometimes it takes longer, so it's important to capture this information as well as how intense the symptoms are. For example:

- After using any devices or specific services enabled on them (Bluetooth, Wi-Fi, GPS, LTE, etc.)
- After spending time in certain areas (office, area of a building, restaurant, etc.)
- Places where there's a lot of Wi-Fi (number of people in a room, near a cell tower or cell panels on the roof, or wireless access points if you're inside)

Step 3: Track how your body feels before, during, and after symptoms.

Start listening to your body. It's important to know how you feel before a trigger occurs because if your immune system was down (e.g., maybe you had a cold or had a health issue flare up) it makes you more susceptible to a reaction.

When you encounter a trigger, usually you start feeling it as the effects become more pronounced. The goal is to feel the subtle warning signs and symptoms listed above before they develop into a full-blown EMF trigger.

How you feel or the area where you feel pain or sensitivity afterward is also important because it might be different depending on the type of EMF field.

Step 4: Track your recuperation.

You need to know how long it takes you to feel better, what actions you took to speed up your recuperation, and whether they worked.

Step 5: Manage your symptoms.

This is where the power of data comes in! Reviewing your journal, you can start seeing patterns to identify:

- What are the different warning signs that your body is giving you?
- What fields trigger you?
- What recuperation methods work for you?
- How long does it take you to recuperate?

These will help you identify what to stay away from when you're out of the house, hear your body's warning signals, and take the right recuperation steps to minimize your downtime.

Cars and EMF Fields

EMF fields in cars can be especially challenging because of the ever-increasing wireless transmitters in such a tiny space.

It's extremely challenging to find a low-EMF car these days, but there are features you can look for and strategies for doing test drives.

Use the following checklist to help you identify what cars may work for you:

- ❑ What features are in the car that transmit, and where are they located? (e.g., Bluetooth, radio frequency, wireless, or radar)
- ❑ Can these features be turned off? For example:
    - Parking assist
    - Blind spot
    - Lane keeper sensors
    - Sunroof—does it have a hard cover (even if it's plastic) to help absorb outside fields from coming through? A fabric

"shade" versus a hard cover that slides can make a difference if you're sensitive.

- Dual sunroofs in the front and back also increase the amount of radiation that can come in from cell towers, so a single sunroof (or none) is better.
- It's worth comparing tinted and non-tinted windows; if you're sensitive, tinted windows may be more helpful.

For test drives, do the following:

- ❑ Have the salesperson disable all wireless, Bluetooth, etc. and then verify with your phone it cannot find the network or pair the device
- ❑ Keep all cell phones off
- ❑ No wearable tech (you may not have any, but the salesperson might!)

I recommend doing only one test drive per day and not doing them two or more days in a row so you can validate any symptoms within twenty-four hours if they don't show up immediately.

Electric and Hybrid Cars

Electric and hybrid cars are great for the environment, but the battery produces a high magnetic field, often located toward the back of the car. Children sitting in the back seats will be the closest to the battery and magnetic fields.

The battery chargers are another source that needs to be taken into consideration. The magnetic fields at the car can easily be 1,000 milligauss while charging! Chargers inside the house will also create very high fields on the walls they are mounted on and the floors directly above. If the charger is outside, the underground line supplying power to the charger can also create stray fields.

I typically recommend avoiding electric and hybrid cars if possible, especially if you're sensitive to EMF fields.

Find a Low-EMF Home

Finding a low-EMF home might seem impossible, but there are strategies you can take to help you find a home with lower-EMF fields and minimal impact on critical spaces such as bedrooms and offices.

Below is a list of items to check as you're looking for a new residence. These are deal-breaker items I share with clients who are looking for a new home.

The following are critical to avoid:

Cell towers

- ❑ No towers in direct line of sight
- ❑ No towers taller than 100 feet on hills directly above
- ❑ No cell panels on building next door (e.g., walls facing the unit or roof) or across the street

Power lines

- ❑ Avoid overhead power lines if possible
- ❑ No power lines or transformers directly next to building or unit (bedroom, living room) or where you spend a lot of time

Utility drops

- ❑ No building utility drop wires on outside walls (for condos, townhomes)
- ❑ No utility drops into ceiling or external bedroom walls

Small cells

- ❑ No small cells on power lines, utility poles etc. outside unit windows

Smart meters

- ❑ Analog preferred
- ❑ No smart meters on living space walls or bedrooms
- ❑ No banks of smart meters with meters pointing at house

Breaker boxes

- ❑ No breaker boxes directly above or below bedroom or living room
- ❑ No breaker boxes in bedroom
- ❑ No breaker boxes on other side of bedroom walls

Other

- ❑ No routers in bedroom
- ❑ No smart technology (wireless security systems, doorbells, heating, etc.)
- ❑ No bedrooms above garage doors
- ❑ No electric bus lines or railways outside the house
- ❑ No power substations within a few blocks (minimum)
- ❑ No satellites attached to the house unless the cables can be removed and are not hot
- ❑ No solar panels on house

Avoiding EMF fields outside of your home is a completely different story. It's not your personal space, and oftentimes you have very little control over your surroundings. In the following section, you'll find out all of my secrets for staying safe when I'm traveling, whether it's a quick overnight stay or longer jaunts for several days.

Travel Tips

I love traveling, exploring new places, and experiencing different cultures, but having EMF sensitivities can make that a lot more difficult. However, there are ways you can reduce your exposure when you're traveling.

Here are the things I've learned over the years that have helped me the most.

On the Plane

Traditionally, the window seat has had higher EMF fields, but that was before there were outlets installed into the back of the seats and before Wi-Fi was available in flight. Most likely there isn't a difference between window or aisle seats today when it comes to EMF exposure.

I do recommend avoiding the wings (another thing I learned through trial and error). The engines create huge magnetic fields, so if you're sitting in a window seat above or within a row or two of the engine, you're going to be exposed to high magnetic fields. Since I've started avoiding sitting within two rows of the wings, I haven't had any EMF triggers.

Traveling With Family or Friends?

If you're traveling with a large group of people, one strategy is to book seats behind you and ask your friends not to use the outlets to eliminate the extra AC direct and magnetic fields literally at your back.

Hotel Rooms

You can easily get overpowered by all of the Wi-Fi from sources both inside and outside your room when staying in a hotel. Choosing a hotel based on location and a room with minimal EMF fields is the best thing you can do to minimize exposure.

Step 1: Minimize your exposure before booking.

1. Search on Antennasearch to identify cell towers or antennas in close proximity and find the one that is the least impacted.
2. Check there aren't any antennas on the roof of the hotel itself.
3. Try to avoid staying at the least-expensive hotels with the thinnest walls, if possible; thin walls allow wireless signals to penetrate more easily. This is true no matter the source, whether it's cell towers and antennas or Wi-Fi routers inside the hotel.

Step 2: Book a low-EMF room.

1. If there are towers or antennas in the area you can't escape (which can be difficult if you're close to the airport or in a cluster of hotels), figure out which side of the hotel is the least impacted and request a room on that side of the building.
2. Try to locate the routers and get a room as far away as possible.
    - If the routers are not at the end of the hallways, getting a room at the end of the hallway usually means you don't have a room on both sides of you exposing you to Wi-Fi coming through.
3. Are there trees on the property? If so, they will help block any EMF fields coming in from the outside from cell towers, cell panels, or power lines.
4. Try to avoid being close to the elevators. They create high magnetic fields, and dirt and dust are stirred up every time the

elevator goes up and down. Being in close proximity means those particles can get into your room much easier.

Step 3: Clear fields in the room.

Once you're in the hotel room, you're confined to a small space with lots of electronics. The following tips will help you while you're there:

- Unplug things closest to the bed.
- Unplug cordless phones (if it's a traditional landline and not right next to the bed, I usually just leave them plugged in for convenience).
- Unplug alarm clocks.
- Unplug lamps next to the bed.
- Unplug TVs (most hotels have TVs that continually transmit wireless).
- Unplug refrigerator if it's within a few feet of the bed.

Remember: If you unplug something, make sure to plug it back in before you check out!

Step 4: Optional: Protect yourself from Wi-Fi from outside the room.

One of the things that has saved me many times over the years is traveling with a wide sheet of EMF fabric and a roll of masking tape. It sounds a little weird, but it does work if there are high fields coming in through windows or adjacent rooms.

These come in handy if:

- the room has a smart TV that can't be unplugged (this can happen with immovable wall mounts) that the fabric can be draped over.
- a cell tower or antenna transmitting through windows. The

fabric can be taped up to cover the windows for a temporary curtain.

- a neighboring unit is transmitting a TON of radio frequency. Tape the fabric on the offending wall.

Recap

Here's what you've learned in this section:

✓ The importance of being able to recognize EMF symptoms before they're permanent

✓ Common EMF symptoms

✓ How to track your symptoms so you can know what fields you're sensitive to and how to manage them

✓ Low-EMF travel tips

EMF SYMPTOM TRACKER

Date: ____________________

Location: ____________________

For how long? ____________________

Symptoms you experienced: ____________________

How long did it take to recover? ____________________

What, if anything, did you do to help recover? ____________________

Date: ____________________

Location: ____________________

For how long? ____________________

Symptoms you experienced: ____________________

How long did it take to recover? ____________________

What, if anything, did you do to help recover? ____________________

PART 3

THE EMF MAKEOVER

CHAPTER 9

FIVE STEPS TO A SAFER, HEALTHIER HOME

Congratulations! Now that you've got the basic knowledge you need, you're ready to start mitigating EMF influence in your home.

In this chapter you're going to go through the steps to clear the fields in your home:

1. Create your plan so you get the critical items addressed first.
2. Learn how to reduce all of the fields so you'll know what your options are.
3. Clear the sources outside of the house.
4. Clear the sources inside, room by room.
5. Create your EMF survival plan to help prevent sensitivities and triggers, and minimize your exposure when you're not at home.

Step 1: Create a Doable Plan That Doesn't Leave Out Anything Important

Creating a doable plan from start to finish will serve as your roadmap as you make progress; it can be as broad or detailed as you want. It should be a living document that you can modify as you progress to allow for changes.

A solid plan and systematic approach ensures nothing critical is missed or left out so you won't have to worry about going back and redoing your work. Having a solid plan keeps you from falling into the trap of starting out all gung ho and then getting completely overwhelmed. It's the difference between going to the grocery store when you're hungry and buying things haphazardly versus planning a few meals, creating a list, and then going to the store.

1. Set aside the time.

How much time do you want to set aside? And how often do you want to work on this? The most important thing is that it's doable so you don't struggle to finish.

Once you figure out how much time to set aside, schedule it in! Whether it's in your day planner or an online calendar, get it scheduled.

I am going to set aside ______________________________
for clearing EMFs.

2. Know what's critical to address.

Knowing what's critical to address in your home helps you prioritize what to do first and keeps you from getting completely overwhelmed.

It's critical to address the following items:

- Outside sources in higher-priority rooms
- Net current
- Bedrooms
- Rooms where you spend a significant amount of time, including:
    - Hotspots in those rooms (e.g., a desk with lots of electronics close at hand)
    - Devices you are around for a significant amount of time (e.g., a cell phone)

3. Prioritize the rooms.

List the rooms where you spend more than a few hours at a time. These should be higher priority. For example, bedrooms are usually at the top of the list because you most likely spend six to eight hours there.

1.
2.
3.
4.
5.
6.
7.

File this list away and use it to prioritize the order in which you remediate your home.

4. Plan for more than one iteration.

In many cases it's impossible to tackle everything at once, even though you're going room by room.

I recommend keeping a separate list of "future" items to make sure they don't fall through the cracks. For example, if you currently have a wireless router and plan on installing a hardwired connection, it may take some time and planning to get this done, and while it's critical, it would be put on a "future" list.

I also recommend keeping these notes with the room it's associated with so it's all in one place.

5. Organize your notes and track your progress.

Taking a series of notes on this project can quickly create a big messy pile! Creating an organized system to store all your notes will make for a more positive experience.

I personally like the customizable binders that allow you to add in sections and individual papers so you can expand your notes as you make progress. My favorite at the moment are the Martha Stewart Discbound notebooks. They're easy to use, the separate sections have pockets for miscellaneous notes, and they allow you to add individual notes. Plus, they're pretty.

You'll know how to best organize your system, but this is the order I've found most helpful for me:

- Your plan (at the front)
- Outside sources
- Net current
- One section per room

6. Be clear on the things that aren't going to be addressed.

This is important because it prevents what we call "scope creep" in the project management world.

I also recommend tracking what you're *not* going to do in each room in case you need to go back and see why you decided against something.

Once you complete a particular room, it's also easy to mark it as complete.

Once you begin, it's easy to start thinking about things like purchasing meters or shielding, both of which will add on extra time (and complexity).

But if you write down what you intend to tackle later, you can go through each room without getting bogged down. Remember, your first priority is to get your house to safer levels.

Step 2: Reduce the Fields Like a Pro Without Having to Hire One

Reducing and eliminating EMF fields isn't always straightforward because, depending on what those sources are, your options will vary. When it comes to reducing your impact, it usually boils down to these four options:

- Eliminate the source creating the fields.
- Change how you use the product or switch to a lower-radiation product.
- Create distance between you and the source that's emitting the field.
- Shield against the field if possible (this requires accurate measurements and an EMF-specific shielding material).

It's also important to remember that different types of EMF fields behave differently. This means solutions have to address each field individually. If you do something to reduce or eliminate one field, it doesn't necessarily reduce the other fields. For example, if your cell phone is plugged into an outlet and you turn on airplane mode, it still has an AC direct field (it's plugged in), an AC magnetic field (it's powered on), and dirty electricity.

In this section you'll learn where the different fields typically drop off and how they can be eliminated or reduced.

AC Direct

AC direct fields can be one of the easiest fields to eliminate or at least reduce your exposure to because these fields come from wiring in the walls or electronics plugged into an outlet or power strip.

The two main options for eliminating or reducing AC direct fields are to unplug the item or create distance between you and the item or cord.

In order to eliminate the field, you need to eliminate the current. That means turning off the breaker if it's wiring in the wall (usually not an option) or, in most cases, unplugging the item altogether when not in use (e.g., an extension cord or phone charger).

These fields typically drop off the most one to three feet away from the walls (from the wiring), electric cords, and small electronics.

HOW THE FIELD BEHAVES

The field moves outward from the source, and the strength of the field drops off with distance and can be absorbed by materials or go through materials depending on strength of the field. The field strength is fairly consistent.

Most home electronics create fields that drop off after one to three feet.

COMMON SOURCES

- Wiring in the walls
- Anything with a cord that is plugged in (extension cord, TV, cordless phone)
- Outlets
- Power strips
- Light switches
- Lighting (canned and track)
- Appliances
- Breaker boxes
- Power lines
- Utility meter

WHAT YOU CAN DO

- Unplug items with cords (extension cords, lamps, cordless phones, phone chargers) OR create distance ideally three feet away if they can't be unplugged.
- Create distance from the wall ideally one to three feet (e.g., move couch, chairs, etc.).
- Keep items unplugged when not being used.
- For breaker boxes, the best option is to create distance (three to six feet) and spend as little time as possible in that area.
- **Note:** AC direct fields from power lines cannot be mitigated other than to create as much distance as possible from them.

Don't forget: These fields can go through walls if they're strong enough, so create distance if there are sources on the other side.

AC Magnetic

AC magnetic fields are similar to AC direct fields because they can be eliminated or reduced by unplugging the source or creating distance.

The difference with this field is that a battery-operated device on standby (such as a cell phone) creates a magnetic field. The only way to eliminate the field is to completely power off the device.

This field typically drops off one to three feet away from the sources such as wiring in the walls, electric cords, and small electronics.

HOW THE FIELD BEHAVES

The field moves outward from the source in a globe-like fashion, and the strength of the field drops off with distance (e.g., ripples from dropping a rock in water). It can be absorbed by materials and go through them if it's strong enough and the field strength is fairly consistent.

COMMON SOURCE(S)

- Anything plugged into an outlet and powered by electricity
- Anything powered on (electric or battery) even if it's on standby, such as cell phone
- TV
- Cordless phone
- Appliance
- Electric toothbrush charger
- Breaker box
- Power lines
- Utility meter

WHAT YOU CAN DO

- Completely unplug and power off device (no standby mode, no airplane mode).
- All battery-operated items should be completely powered off so they are not active (i.e., turned to airplane mode or standby).
- **Note:** AC Magnetic fields from power lines cannot be mitigated other than to create as much distance from them as possible.

Don't forget: These fields can go through walls if they're strong enough, so create distance if there are sources on the other side.

Radio Frequency

Radio frequency behaves completely different than AC direct and AC magnetic fields. The strength of the field is constantly changing and, while the strength drops off with distance, products that create radio frequency fields—a cordless phone, Wi-Fi router, cell phone, etc.—are designed to travel longer distances, so it's difficult to predict exactly where this field falls off without meters.

The only way to eliminate radio frequency is to prevent the source from transmitting, which usually means completely turning it off (e.g., a cell phone).

Devices that transmit radio frequency—like Bluetooth, GPS, and wireless—can have more than one chip transmitting radio frequency at separate intervals. By disabling these services you can easily reduce the radiation impact.

HOW THE FIELD BEHAVES

The field always changes in strength and behavior and depends on usage. It can be absorbed by materials, bounce and deflect off surfaces (e.g., go around corners and through gaps such as windows or doors), and go through materials.

COMMON SOURCE(S)

- Anything that emits Wi-Fi, Bluetooth, GPS, and cellular signals
- Routers
- Cell phones
- Laptops, tablets, computers
- Cordless phones, baby monitors
- Wireless or Bluetooth speakers (e.g., SONOS)
- Digital personal assistants (e.g., Alexa)
- Wireless streaming media (e.g., Amazon Fire Stick)
- Smart TVs
- Toys
- "Smart" appliances, light switches, etc.

WHAT YOU CAN DO

- Unplug the device that is transmitting (e.g., Smart TV).
- For battery-operated items, you may need to completely power off the device so it is not transmitting or receiving (e.g., cell

phone). And for items like cordless phones or Roku, you may need to remove the batteries.

- Turn off specific services to reduce your impact (e.g., cell phones, Bluetooth, GPS, automatic email), and only turn on when you use them.

A Note about Radio Frequency Shielding Materials: You should never use any type of EMF shielding, whether it's a bed canopy with special fabric or EMF paint, without taking measurements first because you need to know how strong *all* of the fields are. If the radio frequency is stronger than what the material can shield against, it can make things exponentially worse because it traps the signal, which will bounce around and triple or quadruple the original radiation levels.

If the other fields are high, you could make matters worse because the shielding material is conductive and provides a larger path for those fields to travel through, creating more of a problem.

Make sure you have good-quality instruments that can take accurate measurements for all the fields and ensure those measurements fall within the specified range of the shielding material.

Shielding materials and instruments typically involve more advanced and technical expertise to implement. You can learn more about instruments and measuring criteria in the bonus chapter at the end of the book. I also recommend hiring a professional to help you.

Dirty Electricity

It can be challenging to reduce dirty electricity because of the number of sources that can create dirty electricity.

Dirty electricity usually drops off the most one to three feet away from the source, whether it's an outlet, transformer (i.e., the black box on a laptop charging cord that steps down and converts the power so it can be used by the battery), or power strip with multiple chargers in it.

To reduce dirty electricity from your electronics, you need to find and unplug all sources.

> **Note:** Outside sources such as smart meters, solar panels, etc. require additional professional guidance.

HOW THE FIELD BEHAVES

Dirty electricity creates harmonics on AC direct and AC magnetic fields along circuits in the house.

COMMON SOURCE(S)

These items, when plugged in, create dirty electricity:

- Variable speed motors (e.g., washers/dryers, blenders, hairdryers)
- All AC to DC converters (these take electricity and convert it so a laptop or cell phone can run on battery), like the black box on your laptop cord
- Items that step down the power so your device isn't overpowered (e.g., "black boxes" on routers, TVs, small electronics)
- Anything that is plugged in and transmits radio frequency (the higher frequency is overlaid on the electrical circuits and creates harmonics)
- Cordless phones
- Solar panels
- Smart meters

WHAT YOU CAN DO

- Unplug the item from the outlet when it's not actively being used.

Do Dirty Electricity Filters Really Work?

Dirty electricity filters are box-like devices that plug into outlets and help filter out the harmonics. However, AC direct and AC magnetic fields are created by these filters because they require electricity. Also, they clean up the AC direct field harmonics, but they make the magnetic fields worse.

This is problematic for people with EMF sensitivities because it can make them feel worse. Some people don't feel any difference. Some even experience a positive difference.

This means you need to make sure you feel a positive difference with the filters and validate the before and after symptoms. You should also take before and after measurements with a dirty electricity meter.

If you decide to take the plunge and purchase filters, use the following guidelines:

- Validate you do not have any wiring or net current issues; otherwise, you can make things worse!
- Write down before and after symptoms to determine if they help or make you feel worse.
- Purchase filters for one room where you spend at least a few hours a day; I recommend four to six filters to start with.
- Purchase a dirty electricity meter to validate the before and after measurements for the circuits in the room that you are testing with.

Net Current

Net current is the other field that should be tested and remediated if it exists. Net current can be found in both older and newer homes, and I find net current in about 30% of the homes I test.

There aren't options for reducing your exposure to net current because it typically circulates throughout the entire home. In most cases, it will be stronger in certain areas of the home close to the source or sources.

The only way net current can be remediated is for a licensed electrician to fix the source of the issue, whether it's a wiring or grounding issue or current coming in from the outside. If you have net current or wiring or grounding errors, shielding or dirty electricity filters will make it worse and should be avoided.

You can take the following steps, which are net current indicators and can save you quite a bit in troubleshooting if it turns out you have net current in your home.

Step 1: Check for net current indicators.

There are some obvious things that indicate that net current exists and can help identify where the sources are:

- Knob and tube wiring (the only remediation is upgrading to current standards)
- Ungrounded outlets (two prong)
- Outlets that don't work 100% of the time
- Light bulbs that burn out very quickly
- Any electrical panel updates or remodels that have been done on the house can introduce wiring errors
- Mixed wiring of knob and tube and current wiring code standards
- Breaker switches that turn off randomly for no reason

Step 2: Test the outlets.

Faulty outlets are indicators that can be checked easily with an inexpensive outlet checker if you don't mind doing the work yourself. These are less than ten dollars and are plugs with three lights that light up different combinations depending on the type of wiring error. There are error codes written on the plugs, making them easy to use.

If you hire an electrician, they will most likely do this anyway (and charge you for it), so this can save you electrician's fees and help narrow down the sources more quickly.

1. Purchase an outlet tester. Usually, you can get this online or at a local hardware store.
2. Have a pen and a roll of white masking tape handy. (I recommend a wide 2-inch roll.)
3. Starting in the first room, plug the outlet checker into the first outlet.
4. Look at the lights and the code on the checker and write the results on the tape (e.g., "Correct," "Open Neutral," etc.).
5. Rip off that piece of tape and place it above the outlet (this makes it easy to know what the results are, and you will use this for Step 3 if you get any error codes).
6. Repeat with each outlet in every room.

Step 3: Validate breaker switches for bad circuits.

For all the outlets that did not test out "Correct" in Step 2 above, you need to identify the breaker switch that controls that outlet:

1. Identify which breaker switch the bad outlet is connected to by plugging something into it, such as the outlet checker or a night-light, and then turn off each switch until you identify which switch controls the outlet.

   Note: It's important to go through each switch, as you can have incorrect wiring where more than one breaker switch controls that outlet.
2. Write down the breaker switch number on the masking tape.
3. Rip off that piece of tape and place it above the other piece of tape above the outlet.

4. Repeat this process for each "bad" outlet.

   Note: It's also helpful to identify all the outlets on the same breaker switch, as it helps the electrician identify the wiring path and helps with troubleshooting.

Step 4: Test for net current (optional).

Try the following techniques to test for net current and narrow down the sources:

- Small handheld AM/FM radio (instead of being tuned to a radio station, tune the setting so that you hear static)
- Buzz stick, used by many DIYers (you can purchase these or search online to build your own)
- Good-quality AC magnetic meter that can measure less than 1 mG

Note: You will want to verify the outside readings for AC magnetic fields in case you have elevated fields outside that are coming in even when the power is turned off.

If you have an AM/FM radio or a buzz stick, you can test what it will sound like when current is detected with something that's running on battery or powered by electricity, such as a cell phone or light bulb.

To test for net current:

1. Turn all breaker switches off (I recommend turning off each switch and not the house main).
2. Test throughout the house and listen for increased static on the radio or buzz stick, because they will detect current. If you have an EMF meter, it will register readings greater than zero.
3. Write down any areas that indicate net current. I recommend walking room by room, taking notes, and checking along the circuits to see if you have light bulbs that burn out quickly, etc. I also recommend writing down where the fields drop off since

these go along a circuit. You might also use painter's tape to map out longer paths.

Step 5: Reach out to a professional to validate your findings.

If you did not find any first indicators of net current but want to make sure you've done your due diligence, the next step is to hire an EMF specialist or electrician or purchase your own set of meters to continue the detective work.

> **Other Resources:** *Tracing EMFs in Building Wiring and Grounding* by Karl Riley is an excellent book that can help you if you must hire an electrician and find and mitigate net current, grounding, or wiring errors. It's written in language an electrician can understand with specific instructions to fix net current issues.

Now that you've learned how the different fields behave, common sources, and mitigation options, we're ready to start addressing all of the sources outside of the home that are affecting you inside.

Step 3: Minimize Your Exposure from Outside Sources

In this section you're going to learn how to assess and mitigate your exposure from the following outside sources that can impact the EMF fields inside the home:

- Cell towers
- Power lines
- Smart meters
- Solar panels

Cell Towers

Assessing your impact from cell tower radiation can be fairly straightforward if you know what to look for and what to be concerned about.

The taller the tower, the farther the cell signal and radiation can transmit without being obstructed by buildings and trees. The number of panels and square boosters mounted on the tower indicates how strong the signals are. More panels and more boosters mean more radiation that can travel farther distances.

It's also important to take note of the tower height (e.g., 100+ feet); it may currently have one tier of panels installed but have room to add more tiers or layers in the future. Towers that are 200–300 feet tall and are over a mile away could very well be impacting your home.

Step 1: Identify cell towers and antennas in your neighborhood with Antennasearch.

1. Boot up your computer and launch a browser.
2. Go to http://www.antennasearch.com and enter your address.
3. View cell tower results to determine the towers that might have radiation coming in through the ceiling of your home:
    a. Filter by 2 miles to find the taller towers that are most likely impacting your house from a distance. Set the filter to 2 miles and note towers 100–150 feet in relation to your home. If you're in a flat area, note towers over 80–100 feet.
    b. Filter down to 1–2 miles and then down to about 0.5 miles away from your home and note where towers are in relation to your home. If you live in a hilly area with lots of mature trees, you probably don't need to worry as much about towers less than 40 feet in height.
4. Go back to the search results tab and select to view the antenna results:
    a. Filter by about a mile and note where the tallest (and

   highest concentration of) antennas are and if your house is impacted.

   b. Continue to zoom in the results by 0.5 miles to several blocks, noting where they are in relation to your home.

5. Using the cell tower and antenna data you've just collected, map out where your house is potentially impacted by cell tower radiation (e.g., the roof, one side of the house, etc.).

Step 2: Check Antennasearch results by touring the neighborhood.

1. Search the old-fashioned way by walking or driving around your neighborhood to find the cell towers near you. Validate Antennasearch findings and add anything new.

Step 3: Check Architecture of Radio results (optional).

1. If you want to validate all of your findings with real-time data and are open to using a wireless connection on your smartphone, you can use the Architecture of Radio app to give you this information.

Note: If you are sensitive to EMF fields, I do not recommend this particular step.

Step 4: Minimize your exposure.

Consider the following steps to minimize your exposure from cell tower radiation:

- Cell towers impacting rooms on top floors: For rooms you spend a significant amount of time in—a few hours or more per day—move to another room on a lower floor if possible and try to avoid spending time in rooms and areas that are impacted the most.
- Cell towers in direct line of sight: Windows do not provide any protection, so if a window faces a cell tower, your best course

of action is to move to a room on a lower floor that does not face the tower.

- Shorter cell towers or antennas: Tall trees and greenery help to block and absorb the radiation for the shorter towers and antennas. If you have shorter towers or antennas near you, planting trees that do not lose their leaves in the winter will help shield against the fields.

Note: If your house is significantly impacted by cell towers (e.g., if you can see a tower from your rooms and it's fairly close or you know that there are large towers above your house that are affecting the top floor), consider purchasing a quality radio frequency instrument or hiring a professional to take measurements and determine what the levels are both outside and inside the rooms of the house. You may want to consider shielding.

Power Lines

It's important to reduce your exposure as much as you can because these fields can easily go through your house, especially if you have overhead power lines. Power lines cannot be shielded, so the best course of action is to create as much distance as possible in the areas where you spend the most amount of time.

Below are the steps to take to mitigate your exposure to power lines.

Step 1: Determine what type of power lines you have.

Are they overhead or underground?

Step 2: Write down the characteristics.

All of the characteristics below indicate how strong the fields are from the power lines.

1. For overhead power lines, ask:

- How tall are the poles and the lines? The taller the pole, the more distance is required for the fields to fall off because the top lines are typically high frequency (i.e., more current).

- Are there a lot of lines? How many levels of wires are there? Are they thin or thick?
- Are there any sections of silver disks? How many, and are there different levels? Silver disks indicate stronger current and require more distance for the fields to fall off.
- Are there any gray transformer buckets attached to the power poles? How many? Ideally, you won't have any buckets, but if you do, it means higher amounts of stray voltage from them.
- Is there anything else attached to the power pole?

2. For underground power lines, ask:

- Where is the square green post where your electricity comes in? Is there just one? These are typically about two feet high and about six inches square somewhere along your property line.
- Is there also a large green square box that services other houses? If you have one of these, it indicates stronger fields and greater distance required for the fields to fall off. Ideally this is not in close proximity to the house.
- Where are the green posts for your neighbors? (This is the path for the underground cables; the fields will be higher there.)

Note: If you live on a corner lot, include observations for both sides of the house that may have power lines running along them.

Step 3: Determine how your house is being impacted.

1. Are there areas outside directly under or above the power lines or within six feet (e.g., patio furniture or play areas)?
2. How far are they from the house?
3. What rooms are closest to these (consider all floors if there is more than one)?

4. Where does the service drop come in?
5. How much time is spent in these rooms?

Step 4: Minimize your exposure.

- Try to avoid outdoor furniture or children's play areas in the direct line or path of the lines either above or below them.
- Try to stay at least thirty feet (preferably more) from the lines.
- Minimize metal furniture if possible (it conducts and amplifies the fields).
- Try to spend as little time as possible in rooms with power lines right outside, especially if there are windows. If you must spend time in rooms where power lines are next to the wall or in close proximity, create as much distance as possible from them.
- If there is a service drop on any bedroom walls, try to move the bedroom to another room if possible. If you can't, moving the bed as far away as possible is the next best option.

Utility Meters

It's important to assess utility meters because they typically produce high AC direct and magnetic fields right at the meter, which can affect the immediate surrounding areas. If you have a digital meter, the radio frequency that is produced can easily go inside the house.

Follow the steps below to minimize your exposure to utility meters:

Step 1: Determine the utility meter location.

Find where the meter is located:

- Is it on the other side of a wall in a room where you spend a significant amount of time?
- Or directly above or below?
- Along the same wall?

Step 2: Determine what type of meter you have.

Is it a smart meter, stealth meter, or (hopefully) an analog meter?

Step 3a: If you have an analog or stealth meter:

1. Find out when your utility company is planning a smart meter deployment (also called digital meters or AMI meters).
2. Is there an opt-out program you can sign up for? What are the costs?

Step 3b: If you have a smart meter:

1. Find out from your utility company if there is an opt-out program and the associated costs. I recommend opting out if that's an option for you. If you rent, you'll most likely need the owner's permission to opt out.
2. Do your neighbors have smart meters pointing into your space? If so, which areas are impacted?
    a. Areas outside where you or your children spend time.
    b. Windows directly facing the meter, including windows that are a floor or two above. If so, I recommend trying to convince your neighbors to opt out or purchase a smart meter guard and ask their permission to place it over theirs. It will not eliminate the radiation, but it will reduce it.

Note: You can also search to find out if you have a local smart meter group that should have the most current smart meter information.

Step 4: Minimize your exposure from smart meters and stealth meters.

Decide which option is best for you:

1. Opting out
2. Shielding (applies to both stealth meters and smart meters)
    - If your city doesn't have an opt-out program, or if you

aren't able to opt out, the next best option is shielding against the smart meter or stealth meter with a meter guard. Smart meter shields allow enough radio frequency to pass through so that the utility company still receives your usage data.

- Depending on the type of smart meter you have and the amount of radiation that's generated, the shields may only reduce the radiation and not eliminate it.
- There are a variety of smart meter guards you can purchase but be sure to look for the following features: You need to know the thresholds of radio frequency it can shield against and how easily it can be installed. Is it something you can do yourself or will you need help?

3. Shielding the back side of the smart meter
    - Shielding the interior walls of the home from smart meter radiation is important if you spend a lot of time in those rooms. Unless the smart meter has RF shielding on the back (most do not), radio frequency will emit from the back and go through the wall it is mounted on.
    - It's recommended you get measurements to see how high the fields are coming into your living space. Windows next to the smart meter or on the floors above or below will be directly impacted.
    - If you want to shield in the interior space, I recommended you purchase a meter or work with a professional so you know what levels the fields are at and what shielding materials are best for your situation.

Can I Move My Smart Meter?

In some cases, you can work with an electrician to get your meter and utility drop moved to a better location.

Smart Meter Banks

If you have smart meter banks in your building, there is usually very little you can do to shield against those fields. They usually come into your entire home, and multiple meters mean that multiple signals are sent out simultaneously 24/7. While you may be able to shield the bedroom, it can be difficult to reduce the rest of the areas (especially with open floor plans).

This can happen whether the smart meters are grouped by each floor or if they're all in one location and the fields are coming into your living area.

In these situations, I recommend getting measurements so you can see how often the signals are being generated and how strong the fields are. Then work with a professional to see if shielding is an option.

Service Drops and Breaker Boxes

Service drops and breaker boxes go hand in hand with utility meters because they're usually grouped together. You should know where they are and how they impact you because:

1. The service drops attach on the exterior, usually along the top of a floor with electrical lines that run vertically or horizontally (sometimes both), which creates a "line" of stray fields on the inside wall.
2. These fields are difficult to shield against because they usually run both vertically and horizontally along the whole wall.
3. If your breaker box is in a living area, it is against building code to block access to a breaker box, so shielding is not an option unless you can have a custom solution built.
4. If you take measurements and decide to shield, those materials are generally optimized for only one field:

  - There are two fields to shield against, AC magnetic and AC direct.
  - AC magnetic shielding is very unwieldy and difficult to work with (G-Iron Flex) and may not reduce the field significantly.
  - AC direct shielding can be addressed with the permanent radio frequency paint or RF mesh; both materials would need to be grounded.

5. The best course of action is to create as much distance as possible if you spend quite a bit of time in these areas.

Solar Panels

Solar panels are a great way to cut down on the amount of energy we consume, but they create all sorts of problems in terms of dirty electricity and magnetic fields.

The panels can cycle every few minutes depending on what the settings are.

If you have solar panels installed:

- Try to install them on a building separate from the house to eliminate your impact. A great solution would be an external garage or shed.
- Try to use panels that have a pure sine wave inverter, which will mostly eliminate the dirty electricity fields.
- Make sure you do not spend time in the same room where the panels are installed because the magnetic fields will extend down eight feet or more.
- If you do not have pure wave inverters, look at whole-house dirty electricity solutions to help clean up the dirty electricity (avoidance is the only option for addressing the magnetic fields).

Satellite Dishes

Satellite dishes are unique because radio frequency radiation is only created when they are actively used. The shape of the dishes causes a high scatter rate, meaning the radiation "scatters" and bounces off the dish and can affect other areas close by.

If you live in a townhouse, condo, or apartment, check how close a neighbor's satellite dish is and if it's pointed in such a way that radiation may be coming through a window when it's being used. Satellite dish cables can create AC direct and AC magnetic field concerns because of the electric current running through them, which can impact your living space. I recommend avoiding satellite dishes if possible.

> **Note:** Check for cables from previous occupants because sometimes they are still creating fields. I recommend you remove them if they're not being used.

Outside Sources and Fields Cheat Sheet

Use the following checklist to guide your outside inspection:

- ❑ **Cell Towers**
- ❑ **Power lines and transformer buckets**
- ❑ **Small cells**
- ❑ **Service utility drop**
- ❑ **Cable drop/cable line**
- ❑ **Phone line**
- ❑ **Gas main**
- ❑ **Utility meter (analog)**
- ❑ **Utility meter (digital)**
- ❑ **Breaker box**

- ❑ **Satellite dish**
- ❑ **Outside security cameras (non-digital)**
- ❑ **Outside security cameras (wireless)**
- ❑ **Solar panels**
- ❑ **Doorbells (wireless)**
- ❑ **Wireless boosters**

Now that all of the outside sources have been identified and mitigated, it's time to start working our way inside the home to address all of the inside sources.

Step 4: Clear the Fields Inside Room by Room

In this section you're going to clear the fields inside your home room by room using a systematic approach. This is the easiest and most thorough way to ensure you don't miss something important.

In this section we'll cover:

- Bedrooms
- Offices
- Living rooms (or family rooms)
- Kitchens

Tracking the Hotspots

One of the tools I recommend is creating a visual of the hotspots in each room you go through. It provides a way to easily visualize where the hotspots are and to track them as you cross items off your list. I recommend doing this for every room and keeping this with your room-specific notes.

Take the following steps for each room we go through in this chapter:

Step 1: Using the template example below, identify the exact location where you spend time.

For example:

- The bed
- A desk
- A couch, chair, chaise, etc.
- A counter or table

Step 2: Draw the items in each room.

Using the EMF Hotspots in the Room template on the following page, sketch items in the room (e.g., a bed, nightstand, etc.).

Step 3: Write down each of the EMF sources impacting that space.

Using the bed as an example, you might write down things like:

- Sources outside (power lines)
- Outlets
- Power strips
- Alarm clocks
- Lamps
- Phone charger
- Baby monitor (or anything wireless)

Step 4: Prioritize the items (optional).

If you want to prioritize, this is the priority that I generally use:

- Top priority 1 = within one to three feet (for any field), anything wireless
- Medium priority = something that should be removed or switched out but can't now
- Low = something in the room that can be switched out (e.g., metal bookshelf) but isn't urgent

Example of bed, nightstands and dresser in a room that would have outlets, lamps, chargers, etc. added to complete the picture.

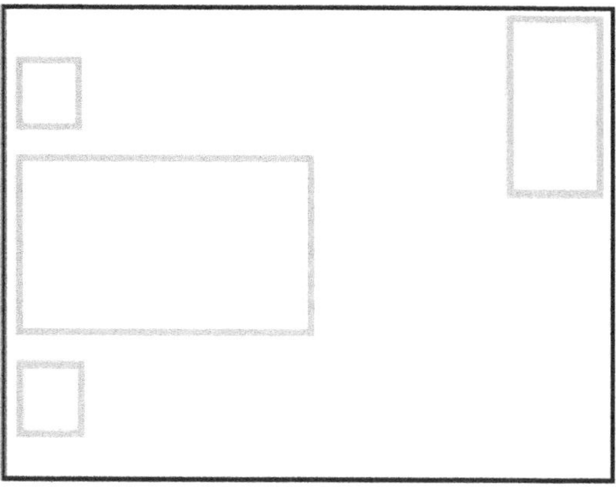

EMF HOTSPOTS IN THE ROOM TEMPLATE

Bedrooms

Bedrooms are the top priority because your body is resting and repairing itself while you're sleeping. And this is a room where you most likely spend at least six to eight hours per day.

EMF fields can significantly reduce the body's melatonin production, which regulates sleep cycles and helps your body fight against disease. In addition, EMF fields trigger the brain into a hyperactive state and initiate the stress response in your body. A low-EMF bedroom is critical for achieving and maintaining good health.

To get the best sleep, here's what you need to do:

- Identify sources coming in from outside and ensure your bedroom is in the best room in the house for optimal sleep.
- Identify sources inside the room and the entire house that affect your sleep and minimize your exposure.
- Reduce metal in the bedroom.

Optimal Bed Placement

There are two things that will help your sleep. First, move the bed so the head is one to three feet away from the wall. This greatly reduces the fields from the wiring in the walls from jumping onto your field and disrupting your sleep. Second, point your bed so the head faces north, which helps the body produce more red blood cells.

Tip: If you have a spouse or other family members who are resistant to turning off Wi-Fi at night, try a seven-day "experiment" and monitor any changes over the week. This is usually a short enough time period they can easily agree to and long enough to see any noticeable improvements that might sway them to do this on a regular basis.

Metal Tanks Your Sleep

Would you be surprised to hear that metal is one of the silent sleep killers that most people don't know about? EMF fields easily travel through metal, and if you have a metal bedframe, box spring, and mattress coils, or metal lamps, these act as conductors for the EMF fields to disrupt your sleep.

The good news is there are easy fixes for this.

Eliminate as much metal as possible within three to six feet of the bed:

- Replace metal bedframes with nonconductive materials such as wood.
- Switch out box spring and mattresses that contain metal with natural latex (not synthetic, as it will off-gas) or organic cotton/wool futon.
- Remove metal lamps next to the bed or replace them with non-metal ones.
- Make sure nightstands next to the bed are not metal.

Extra credit: If you have metal in your bed, there's a quick and easy way to see how much of an impact the EMF fields are making on your body.

You'll need a good-quality oil-filled compass. Don't use a compass on a smartphone or tablet because those can be off by fifteen degrees or more.

1. Hold the compass about an inch above the bed and wait for the needle to settle down.
2. Start moving the compass slowly across the bed from left to right, starting at the head of the bed.
3. Look for areas the compass needle moves fifteen degrees or more (it's not uncommon to see variances greater than fifteen degrees).
4. Repeat this process for the entire bed. The goal is to have fifteen degrees or less variance throughout the entire bed. If there are variances greater than fifteen degrees, you should consider replacing with non-metal materials as soon as you can.

Step 1: Eliminate impact from outside sources.

The best course of action is to try and avoid outside sources, if possible. If you can't, create as much distance as you can from the following items:

- ❑ Visibility to any cell towers from any of the windows
- ❑ Power lines
- ❑ Transformer buckets
- ❑ Small cells on utility poles or power lines
- ❑ Service utility drop (into ceiling or wall)
- ❑ Utility meter (analog or digital smart meter)
- ❑ Cable line
- ❑ Phone line
- ❑ Gas main
- ❑ Water or sewer pumps
- ❑ Air conditioning unit
- ❑ Jacuzzi or hot tubs that are powered on 24/7
- ❑ Outside security cameras
- ❑ Outside wireless boosters
- ❑ Anything that transmits radio frequency

Step 2: Eliminate things next to the bed.

The next step is minimizing things plugged in within three to six feet of the bed because the fields are close enough to "jump" onto your field and disrupt your sleep:

- ❑ White noise machine
- ❑ Nightstand lamps
- ❑ Lamp sconces (next to bed)
- ❑ Alarm clock
- ❑ Cell phone charger
- ❑ Night-lights

- ❑ Extension cords and power strips
- ❑ Fans/air conditioners

Step 3: Eliminate all Wi-Fi in the bedroom.

All wireless devices should be removed altogether or at least completely unplugged at night. This is important because wireless travels several feet, and moving a wireless device across the room will not make much of a difference. Eliminate the following sources of Wi-Fi from bedrooms:

- ❑ Amazon Fire Stick
- ❑ Cable box
- ❑ Alexa (digital assistant)
- ❑ Roku
- ❑ Wireless speakers (SONOS)
- ❑ TV
- ❑ Cordless phone
- ❑ Baby monitor
- ❑ Smart lights
- ❑ Smart switches
- ❑ Security cameras
- ❑ Wireless speakers
- ❑ Fitbits, Apple Watch, etc.
- ❑ Tablets

Step 4: Place the bed in the best location.

Next, you want to make sure the bed is in the best spot in the room.

The bed should be at least three feet or more from any and all of the following because these fields can jump onto your field:

- ❑ Breaker boxes
- ❑ Appliances on other side of wall

- ❑ Three-way light switches
- ❑ Dimmer light switches
- ❑ Traditional light switches
- ❑ Overhead lights/light fixtures
- ❑ Outlets (cable, ethernet)

Sleeping Area Final Checklist

The checklist below will help you track what's been completed and what still needs to be done:

- ❑ **Outside sources have been minimized.** The bedroom is in the best location with the least outside sources affecting it.
- ❑ **The bed is one to three feet from the wall.** All sides of the bed (most important is the head) are at least three feet away from any walls.
- ❑ **No wireless devices in the bedroom are powered on.** No cell phones, TVs, tablets, computers, cordless phones (or baby monitors), or any other wireless transmitting devices are in the bedroom and powered on at night.
- ❑ **Nothing is plugged in next to the bed.** Cell phone chargers, alarm clocks, metal lamps, extension cords, white noise machines, etc. have all been unplugged.
- ❑ **Nothing is plugged in within three to six feet of the bed.** Cell phone chargers, alarm clocks, metal lamps, extension cords, white noise machines, etc. have been moved and unplugged.
- ❑ **You're using a non-metal bedframe.**
- ❑ **Mattress does not contain metal coils or bed springs.**
- ❑ **You're not using a metal box spring.**
- ❑ **No Wi-Fi is turned on in the house at night.** Routers, digital personal assistants (Alexa), security systems, all cell phones, cable boxes, etc. have been turned off.
- ❑ **BONUS:** Bed is arranged with the head facing north.

Home Offices

An office is an important area because this is where we usually have tons of electronics such as modems, routers, printers, power strips, and chargers within close range of our desks.

The great news is that home offices are usually one of the easier areas to reduce EMF fields.

Step 1: Minimize outside sources.

The first thing to do is minimize your exposure from sources outside coming into the office using the following checklist as a guideline.

- ❑ Visibility to cell towers from any of the windows
- ❑ Power lines
- ❑ Transformer buckets
- ❑ Small cells on utility poles or power lines
- ❑ Service utility drop (into ceiling or wall)
- ❑ Utility meter (analog or digital smart meter)
- ❑ Cable line
- ❑ Phone line
- ❑ Gas main
- ❑ Water or sewer pumps
- ❑ Air conditioning unit
- ❑ Jacuzzi or hot tubs that are powered on 24/7
- ❑ Outside security cameras
- ❑ Outside wireless boosters
- ❑ Anything that transmits radio frequency

Step 2: Minimize fields close to the desk.

The next step is minimizing fields from items plugged within arm's reach of the desk. The goal is to create a distance of three feet or more from you:

- [ ] Breaker boxes
- [ ] Appliances on other side of wall
- [ ] Three-way light switches
- [ ] Dimmer light switches
- [ ] Traditional light switches
- [ ] Overhead lights/light fixtures
- [ ] Outlets (cable, ethernet)
- [ ] Lamps
- [ ] Docking stations
- [ ] Chargers (cell phone, laptop, tablet)
- [ ] Cable boxes

Step 3: Rearrange your office to prevent fatigue.

Your office and computer should be arranged to minimize your impact from all the different EMF fields as much as possible.

A typical office usually has the following within arm's reach:

- Computer (desktop or laptop + monitor)
- Modem
- Printer
- Wireless speakers
- Wireless keyboard
- Wireless mouse
- Power strip
- Chargers for phone and laptop
- Desk lamp

And it's usually set up like this:

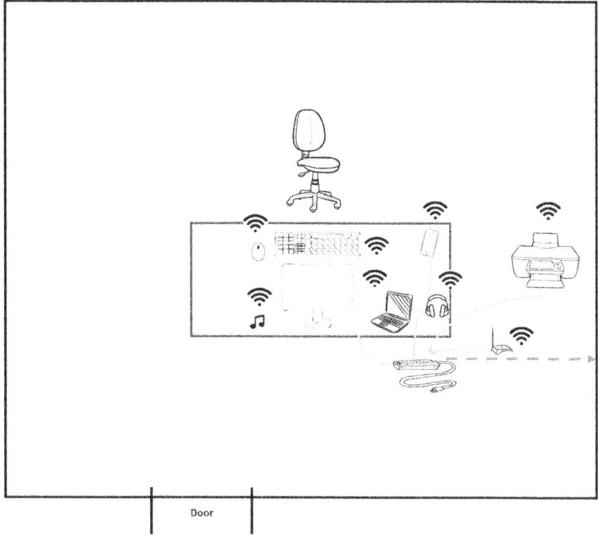

The problem with this arrangement is that you're constantly bombarded by EMF fields that drain your energy and affect your ability to focus and be productive.

The office configuration below is a much healthier option because most of the electronics are moved away from the desk:

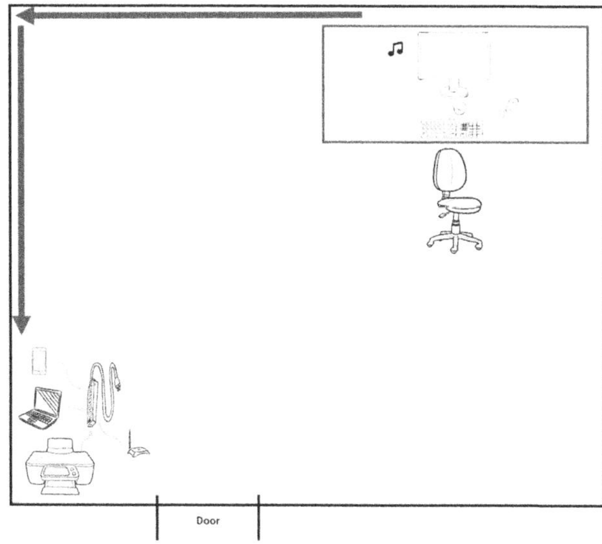

Here's what changed:

- Hardwired internet connection
- Only a monitor, keyboard, mouse, and speakers are on the desk (all hardwired).
- **Note:** Monitors with USB ports will allow you to plug in wired keyboard, mouse, speaker/microphone, and video camera, and speakers.
- Longer cords (for devices such as monitor, docking station connector, etc.) added to distance the desk from the rest of the electronics (listed below), which are moved as far away as possible:
    - Modem
    - Laptop
    - Phone charger is unplugged except when being used
    - Printer is unplugged except when being used
    - Power strip (make sure this is a three-prong plug)

Aim for a distance of six feet from all the cords and everything else that's plugged in across the room.

Avoid creating a "circle" of EMF fields that circle the desk (and you) like the example on the following page:

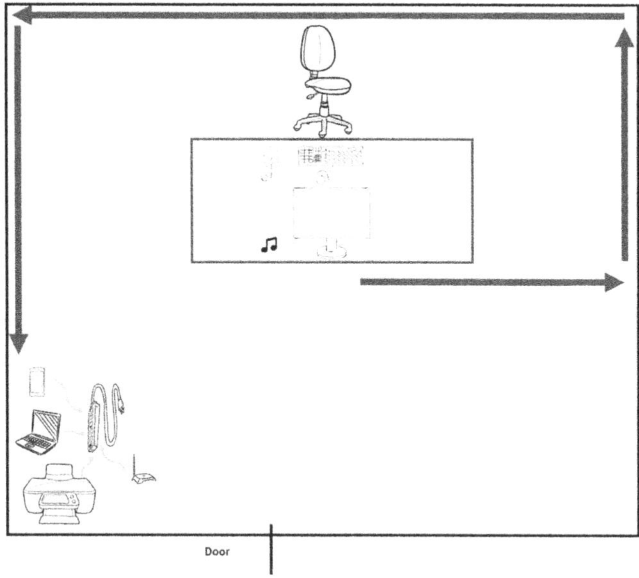

Note: Mac users cannot set up this configuration because the cords are proprietary and don't come in the longer lengths that are needed.

To set up a low-EMF configuration, you need:

- Docking station (ethernet connection, at least two USB ports, and a monitor port for laptop users only)
- Monitor with four USB ports (for mouse, keyboard, speaker, etc.)
- Cable to connect the monitor to the docking station (verify the port types)
- Docking station cable to connect to the monitor (laptop users only)
- Long cable to connect monitor to CPU (verify port type, for CPU users only)
- Wired USB mouse
- Wired USB keyboard

- Optional: longer power cord for the monitor so it can be plugged in across the room

Note: You will use the monitor to plug in the keyboard and mouse and should have two remaining USB ports for speaker/microphones, headsets, video camera, or speakers as needed.

Step 4: Switch out for lower-radiation products.

This next step is important because you're eliminating radio frequency *and* reducing your impact from AC direct and AC magnetic fields and dirty electricity. Use the list below as a starting guideline to switch out or replace with lower-radiation solutions:

- ❑ **Alexa (digital assistant):** Remove
- ❑ **Cordless phone:** Replace with wired VoIP, traditional landline, or Skype number
- ❑ **Wireless headset:** Replace with wired headset or non-Bluetooth/wireless USB speaker/microphone
- ❑ **Wireless or optical keyboards:** Replace with wired keyboard
- ❑ **Wireless or optical mouse:** Replace with wired mouse
- ❑ **Printer:** Replace with non-wireless and disable wireless
- ❑ **Speakers:** Ensure they are wired and any Bluetooth or Wi-Fi is disabled

Tip: One of my secret weapons is a USB wired speaker/microphone, which allows me to disable Bluetooth. I love it because I can log into calls through my computer and never have to pick up a cell or cordless phone!

Office Survival Tips

Minimizing your EMF exposure is essential if you have to go into an office environment on a regular basis, even if it's just a few days a week. Radio frequency is the field to be most concerned about because of all the laptops, tablets, cell phones, and access points (wireless hotspots) that create radiation throughout the building.

The first thing you want to do is assess your office or cube space.

Step 1: Identify fields impacting you from outside.

Windows are great because of the natural light, but they're also an easy way for cell tower radiation to come through.

- Check Antennasearch and do a visual check for cell towers around the building and where they are located. Are there any that could be creating radio frequency that are coming in through windows and into your space?
- Look for power lines, transformers, or smart meters on or near the building or office area. Are there any on the outside walls or near your office?
- Check for any antennas on the roof or along the top floor of the building and notice your relation to them. Are you directly underneath?

Step 2: Identify Wi-Fi sources impacting you.

Unless you have a small office, most buildings don't have just one router; it will have lots of tech-friendly wireless devices, so take inventory and write down what's around you, including:

- Wi-Fi routers
- Access points (on ceilings)
- Wireless security cameras
- TVs and projectors

- Wireless printers
- Neighboring offices

Step 3: Identify areas that have lower-EMF fields impact (optional).

Using the steps and criteria above, you're going to see if there are other areas that aren't as impacted by EMF fields. If your office or cube location is already in an ideal spot, you don't need to do anything. If, however, there are other areas that aren't as impacted by EMF fields, try to move, if possible.

Most offices are optimized for the most efficient use of space, and they can be pretty small areas. This means it's critical to minimize your impact from everything on your desk.

Use the following steps to help you.

A. Optimizing your desk.

- Locate your desk as far away as possible from outlets and switches on the walls.
- If you're in a cube, note where the outlets are not only for your cube but also for your neighbor's space. Outlets can be on your side and on the other side of the wall if they're hardwired in.
- Try to be on an end cube to reduce the number of fields surrounding you.

B. Set up your computer and accessories.

- Mimic the computer configuration for the low-EMF office as much as possible, with the docking station, power strips, chargers, etc. as far away from where you sit as possible.
- Try to have everything hardwired such as headset, mouse, keyboard, and internet connection. Some offices have ethernet ports already set up, so check or ask your IT department if you

can have a hardwired connection. Just remember to turn off wireless and Bluetooth on your computer!

C. Check phone placement and conference calls.

- Try to have the phone as far away from you as possible.
- If you must have a headset, get a wired one instead of using a wireless. (I've measured wireless headsets at 200,000 $\mu W/m^2$!)

Conference rooms are another place where you can get blasted by the fields from everyone's laptops, tablets, and phones—not to mention all the hardwired electronics inside the room itself.

As much as possible, avoid:

- Windows and outside fields coming in from cell towers, power lines, etc.
- Sitting underneath any overhead projectors (especially if they're wireless)
- Light switch panels (especially when there are dimmers)
- The projection screen or TV even if they're only on standby since they can be transmitting radio frequency
- Routers or wireless access points in the room
- Wireless speakers (especially the overhead ones)
- Built-in outlet panels on the table or underneath on the floor
- Outlets on the floor

Tip: Find the lowest-EMF conference rooms in the building or floor so you know which ones to book if you need to set up meetings. This is very important if some of the "nicer" conference rooms with views are in direct line of sight of cell towers or antennas. If you volunteer to set up meetings, you can book these lower-EMF rooms!

The Low-EMF Office Checklist

- ❑ **All outside sources have been minimized.** The office has the fewest number of outside sources affecting it (use checklist from earlier in this chapter).
- ❑ **Distance from light switches and dimmers, outlets (phone, cable, CAT5) is at least three feet.** Moving the desk or working table away from switches reduces impact from AC direct and AC magnetic fields from the wires.
- ❑ **No metal monitor stands, lamps, chairs, or desks.** Avoid these items to prevent EMF fields from conducting through them.
- ❑ **No chargers, power strips, extension cords within three feet of the desk or work table.**
- ❑ **Low-EMF office configuration.** Setup for the main CPU or laptop so it's across the room from your desk/work table.
- ❑ **No Wi-Fi or Bluetooth in the office.** This includes routers, tablets, cell phones, printers, digital personal assistants (Alexa), SONOS, etc.
- ❑ **All computer accessories hardwired.** This includes keyboard, mouse, headsets, speakers.
- ❑ **Blue light from your computer filtered out.** Use either yellow computer glasses, a monitor screen, or have the coating added to your prescription glasses.
- ❑ Plug in **printers** only when using them, and make sure Bluetooth and Wi-Fi are disabled.
- ❑ **Use a hardwired speaker/microphone for conference calls.**
- ❑ **If you must use a headset, use a wired one and keep it plugged in only when using it.**

Things to look for outside the office:

1. **Nearby cell towers or antennas.**

- ❑ www.antennasearch.com
- ❑ Check the building you'll be in AND the buildings next to and across the street for cell panels on the roof or along the top floor external walls.

2. Check the following for the building you'll be in:

- ❑ Utility poles
- ❑ Overhead power lines and number of disks (silver ones indicating more current)
- ❑ Transformer buckets (size and quantity)
- ❑ Small cells (on poles or overhead power lines)
- ❑ Utility service drop (large boxes)
- ❑ Smart meters and direction they're pointing

<u>Things to look for inside the office:</u>

1. Ceilings:

- ❑ Security cameras
- ❑ Wireless access points
- ❑ Lighting systems (e.g., fluorescents, LEDs)

2. Once inside, observe where you are relative to:

- ❑ Light switches and dimmers
- ❑ Satellite security cameras or wireless motion detectors
- ❑ Outlets (and if anything is plugged in)
- ❑ Cordless phones
- ❑ iPad or other tablet registers
- ❑ Lights and lamps
- ❑ Cordless phones
- ❑ Extension cords, power strips, anything with a charger

Living Rooms and Family Rooms

These rooms are often high on the priority list because that's usually where people spend a fair amount of time. A living room or family room also tends to house a lot of electronics such as TVs, game consoles, wireless speakers, and other accessories.

Step 1: Identify outside sources coming into the living room.

You will want to look at the outside sources coming into the living room. Since living rooms are bigger, there's more flexibility when it comes to rearranging furniture so that any areas with higher exposure can be reduced. Check for:

- ❑ Visibility to cell towers from any of the windows
- ❑ Power lines
- ❑ Transformer buckets
- ❑ Small cells on utility poles or power lines
- ❑ Service utility drop (into ceiling or wall)
- ❑ Utility meter (analog or digital smart meter)
- ❑ Cable line
- ❑ Phone line
- ❑ Gas main
- ❑ Water or sewer pumps
- ❑ Air conditioning unit
- ❑ Jacuzzi or hot tubs that are powered on 24/7
- ❑ Outside security cameras
- ❑ Outside wireless boosters
- ❑ Anything that transmits radio frequency

Step 2: Eliminate or minimize Wi-Fi.

Living rooms and family or media rooms can be a little challenging when it comes to reducing Wi-Fi unless you have a hardwired connection set up. The healthiest option is to remove anything that transmits radio frequency. The second-best option is to completely unplug the item unless it's being used, as many items transmit when they're on standby. Check the following:

- ❑ **TVs:** should be unplugged when not in use
- ❑ **Game consoles**
- ❑ **Nest:** Go into Settings menu and disable wireless for all units or replace with a traditional manual thermostat.
- ❑ **Content streaming services (Amazon Fire, Roku, etc.):** Make sure these aren't plugged into the outlet or TV USB port to prevent it from transmitting.
- ❑ **Wireless speakers:** Make sure these are hardwired and that wireless can be fully disabled. If they're connected to a TV, validate the TV wireless settings to make sure that powering on the TV does not override any settings if wireless has been disabled.
- ❑ **Cordless phones**
- ❑ **Wireless vacuum cleaners**

Step 3: Minimize fields close to seating areas.

The next step is to minimize fields next to the chairs and couches that are used the most and create a distance of three feet or more or unplug or remove items, especially if they're only there for decorative purposes. Check the following:

- ❑ Breaker boxes
- ❑ Appliances on other side of wall
- ❑ Three-way light switches
- ❑ Dimmer light switches
- ❑ Traditional light switches

- ❑ Overhead lights/light fixtures
- ❑ Outlets (cable, ethernet)
- ❑ Lamps
- ❑ Cable boxes
- ❑ TVs, game consoles
- ❑ Chargers (cell, laptop, tablet)
- ❑ Power strips

Living Room Checklist

Use this quick checklist to track your living room progress:

- ❑ Outside sources have been minimized
- ❑ Radio frequency has been minimized or eliminated
- ❑ Distance from light switches, dimmers, and outlets is at least three feet
- ❑ Distance from cable outlets, phone outlets, CAT5 outlets is at least three feet
- ❑ Lamps plugged in next to couches, chairs, chaises, are at least three feet away if possible
- ❑ Lamps have been unplugged if they're only for decorative purposes. Lamps can create AC direct fields as high as 700 V/m just by being plugged in.
- ❑ Metal lamps and tables have been minimized.
- ❑ No power strips or chargers next to couches, chairs, chaises
- ❑ Wi-Fi has been minimized in the room; turned on only when devices are in use

Kitchens

Kitchens can be high priority if they are also used for office nooks or islands as a workspace for a laptop. Kitchens tend to have a lot of large and small appliances as well.

Step 1: Identify outside sources coming into the kitchen.

You will want to look at the outside sources coming into the kitchen, but since the wall space can be taken up by appliances, shelving, and cabinets, your options for minimizing the fields may be fairly limited, and you might only be able to focus on seating areas or places where you stand such as the sink or counter.

- ❑ Visibility to cell towers from any of the windows
- ❑ Power lines
- ❑ Transformer buckets
- ❑ Small cells on utility poles or power lines
- ❑ Service utility drop (into ceiling or wall)
- ❑ Utility meter (analog or digital smart meter)
- ❑ Cable line
- ❑ Phone line
- ❑ Gas main
- ❑ Water or sewer pumps
- ❑ Air conditioning unit
- ❑ Jacuzzi or hot tubs that are powered on 24/7
- ❑ Outside security cameras
- ❑ Outside wireless boosters
- ❑ Anything that transmits radio frequency

Step 2: Eliminate or minimize Wi-Fi.

It can be somewhat easier to reduce Wi-Fi in a kitchen because of the amount of space available, and devices in the kitchen are usually portable, brought in only temporarily. The healthiest option is to remove anything that transmits radio frequency. The next best option is to keep devices completely unplugged or on airplane mode with wireless services disabled. Use the following checklist in your kitchen:

- ❑ Smart appliances should have wireless disabled
- ❑ Microwave ovens should be replaced with portable convection ovens or electric tea kettles
- ❑ Digital personal assistants (e.g., Alexa) should be removed altogether or unplugged when not being used
- ❑ Nest: Go into Settings menu and disable wireless for all units or replace with a traditional manual thermostat
- ❑ Wireless speakers: Make sure these are hardwired and that wireless can be fully disabled (even hardwired wireless speakers can still transmit in the background)
- ❑ Cordless phones
- ❑ The healthiest option with cell phones, laptops, and tablets is to keep them completely powered off or on airplane mode with all wireless disabled
- ❑ Security cameras should be removed or replaced with a non-wireless setup
- ❑ Wireless door locks should have wireless disabled or replaced with a non-wireless option

Step 3: Minimize fields close to seating areas.

The next step is to minimize fields next to tables and kitchen island counters and create a distance of three feet or more or unplug or remove items, especially if they're only there for decorative purposes. Check for the following:

- ❑ Breaker boxes
- ❑ Appliances
- ❑ Three-way light switches
- ❑ Dimmer light switches
- ❑ Traditional light switches
- ❑ Overhead lights/light fixtures
- ❑ Outlets (cable, ethernet)
- ❑ Chargers (cell phone, laptop, tablet)
- ❑ Small appliances that are plugged in but not used regularly (blenders, mixers, etc.)

Kitchen Checklist

Use this quick checklist to track your kitchen progress:

- ❑ Outside sources have been minimized
- ❑ Distance from light switches, dimmers, outlets is at least three feet. Moving your furniture away from switches will prevent the AC direct and AC magnetic fields from the wires from jumping onto your field.
- ❑ Distance from outlets is at least three feet
- ❑ Distance from cable outlets, phone outlets, CAT5 outlets is at least three feet
- ❑ No chargers plugged in within three feet of tables, breakfast nooks, or breakfast bars, etc.
- ❑ Metal furniture and accessories have been minimized

- ❑ Wi-Fi from cordless phones, baby monitors, tablets/computers (for workspaces) has been removed
- ❑ No microwave ovens or inductive stoves
- ❑ No smart appliances (or wireless has been disabled)
- ❑ No cordless phones

This, my smart and savvy reader, is where most people pop the champagne cork and celebrate that they've finished remediating EMFs in their home, and that's all they need to do.

Step 5: Create Your EMF Survival Plan

There's one final step, though, that I encourage you to take. I find this makes all the difference in maintaining lasting and effective protection against EMF exposure.

This last step is all about creating your personal EMF survival plan. Each person's setup will vary depending on how much from each component they want to integrate into their life.

I suggest starting off by implementing one thing from each of the categories below. The key thing here is to make it doable. Don't overload yourself and burn out! And remember that every action adds up and contributes to your wellness.

- Technology plan
- Diet and nutrition
- Natural solutions
- Planning for when you're not at home

If you have EMF sensitivities, I also recommend following the guidelines for managing your sensitivities in Chapter 8.

I recommend starting a journal to track how you're feeling and what changes you are making so you can go back and see what things helped the most and what things didn't.

Creating Your Technology Plan

Rethinking how you use technology and rely on your devices is crucial because of the number of electronics we have in our homes and offices.

The goal of a technology plan is simple: reduce the amount of time you're exposed to fields from your electronics and increase your distance from them as much as possible.

This approach will help you make informed decisions with a systematic approach without feeling like you need to toss every device in your life.

A good technology plan includes:

- Identifying areas you spend an hour or more each day and which electronics are within a few feet of those areas
- Reducing the number of fields impacting you in those areas
- Reducing the amount of time you're exposed to those fields

A poor technology plan consists of randomly turning things off or unplugging electronics when the thought crosses your mind. If you don't change anything or you change things randomly, you won't create the significant effects you need to improve your health.

Step 1: Identify your high-EMF areas.

Write down where you spend the most amount of time and at least an hour each day (or each visit; for example, you may not be in your home office every day, but when you are there, you spend at least two hours).

Write down the devices within a few feet of where you sit. Include all radio frequency devices even if they're more than a few feet away.

Step 2: Don't forget your portable devices.

1. Write down all the devices you typically carry with you or that you're around for at least an hour every day, such as a cell phone or laptop.

2. Write down how you use these:

- Is it plugged in while you're using it?
- Is it transmitting radio frequency all the time?
- What other services are always turned on?
- Where is it? Right next to you or in a pocket? In a purse? Across the room from you?

Step 3: Create your technology plan.

Write down how you're going to reduce your impact, starting with the rooms you spend the most time in:

- Eliminate fields by unplugging something. For example, unplugging a phone charger when it's not being used eliminates dirty electricity, AC direct, and AC magnetic fields.
- Increase distance from electronics to reduce impact from the fields. For example, move a power strip that's right next to where you sit to across the room.
- Decrease the amount of time or how often the device is powered on and used. For example, only plug in a printer when it's actively used.
- Switch out for a lower-radiation product. For example, change from a Bluetooth headset to a wired non-Bluetooth headset.
- Change a setting on a cell phone. For example, disable GPS and Bluetooth on your cell phone.
- Change how you use your device. For example, use speakerphone instead of a Bluetooth headset with a cell phone.

Technology Plan

Date:

Room/Item:

I am going to …

This will benefit me by …

Date:

Room/Item:

I am going to …

This will benefit me by …

Date:

Room/Item:

I am going to …

This will benefit me by …

Supplementing Diet and Nutrition

For starters, I recommend looking at the clean-eating and detoxing principles regarding hydration and foods to avoid, since those are what I call low-hanging fruit.

Then I recommend working with your healthcare professional before making any changes to your existing diet to determine the best solutions for you.

And don't forget to track everything!

Natural and Holistic Solutions

Adding natural, holistic solutions is one of my favorite parts of EMF management! It's important to pay attention to your symptoms if you have them. If you don't have EMF symptoms, I recommend experimenting with a few solutions that resonate with you and sticking with the ones that make you feel the best.

When I was extremely sensitive and dealing with pain in my neck and jawline, a weekly lymphatic massage gave immediate relief, and the treatment would "hold" for about a week afterward. Later on, after my sensitivities had subsided significantly and I was working in a different office environment, I switched to sound bowl therapy because it seemed to help the most.

Don't be afraid to try something new. Don't worry that something has gone wrong if your current solution starts to feel like it's not working as well as it has in the past. Your body might just need a change.

Leaving Home

This, in my opinion, is a nonnegotiable component whether you have sensitivities or not.

The key here is to plan for exposure when you're out of the house. Know how long you'll be gone, how much you're going to be exposed to, and what you can do to minimize your exposure.

These are some of the tactics I use when I'm out and about:

- Check Antennasearch before heading out.
- Look at the building or location surroundings to see where the hotspots are such as power lines, smart meters, or cell towers.
- Once you're inside, look for things that might cause triggers such as wireless access points (usually on the ceilings), routers, fields coming in through a window (if you're seated next to a window).

Have a mini-recuperation plan built in, whether it's eating some protein, making a salt scrub, or meditation after you get home.

The goal is to get in the habit of planning so you won't get caught off guard. Eventually, this will become a habit you don't think twice about.

Your Technology Plan

My technology plan includes:

I'm going to make the following changes to my nutrition:

Holistic and natural solutions I am going to start incorporating:

When I'm out of the house I'm going to:

Recap

Here's what you've learned in this section:

- ✓ How to create a solid, achievable plan to clear the EMFs in your home
- ✓ How all of the different fields behave, common sources, mitigation options, and where the fields typically start to drop off
- ✓ How to do the first steps for detecting net current
- ✓ Step-by-step instructions for minimizing outside sources including cell towers, smart meters, stealth meters, analog meters, solar panels, power lines, service drops
- ✓ Room-by-room instructions for clearing the fields
- ✓ How to set up your bedroom for the best sleep
- ✓ How to set up a low-EMF office
- ✓ How to set up a low-EMF kitchen and family room
- ✓ Why you need a personal EMF survival plan and what you should include
- ✓ How to create your EMF survival pan

BONUS: EMF INSTRUMENTS

Do you need EMF meters to make a difference? I remember wondering the same thing. I had no idea what to get or how to make an informed decision!

The truth is, in many cases, you don't need a meter to start making changes that will benefit your health.

I typically recommend *not* purchasing meters when you're first learning about EMF fields because it can be completely overwhelming to learn the fields in general, figure out the meters, and translate the measurements into actionable steps.

It's better to build a solid foundation of knowledge about the fields and how they work as you mitigate your own environment. Once you've established that foundation, it will be much easier to incorporate instruments to fine-tune your solutions.

There aren't any shortcuts to understanding how to use the meters and interpret the readings. Most people make the mistake of buying meters that light up a color (red, green, yellow) or thinking they can figure them out once they start using them. The problem is the red, green, yellow system is usually a specified range, and that range doesn't necessarily correspond to the color when it comes to health concerns. For example, a meter might show the reading as being in the green (safe) category according to FCC standards, but from a Building Biology guidelines perspective or thresholds where biological effects are expected, it should actually be in a red or unsafe category. Secondly, you need to be familiar with the units of measurement by field (think of this as how strong the EMF field is), the measurement and severity categories, and what to do. And all of this takes time.

Meters are good for:

- Taking before and after measurements as you clear the fields in your home
- Making inside versus outside comparisons
- Using shielding, whether it's temporary (fabric curtains or bed canopies) or more permanent solutions (window film or EMF paint)
- Measuring specific items such as cell phones or modems
- Showing your spouse or child if they need convincing to reduce their exposure
- Determining the severity category of your home

Once you are comfortable with your knowledge of the fields and have started to make changes, I recommend getting a good-quality combined AC direct and AC magnetic meter that is accurate and then purchasing a separate radio frequency meter. It's better to save your money and purchase one meter at a time so you won't need to change them out and upgrade later.

All-in-One Meters

These measure AC direct, AC magnetic, and radio frequency in one meter. They're usually the least expensive and can be good if you just want to dip your toes in the water and are not too concerned with accurate measurements.

While they're convenient, the level of accuracy is the biggest issue, which is why I recommended getting separate meters.

Decide Which Meters to Purchase

Knowing which meters to purchase can be overwhelming. How do you determine which ones are the best fit for you with all of the available choices? And price points can range from $50–$100 or more.

First of all, you don't need to spend thousands of dollars to get a decent meter that takes accurate measurements. On the other hand, don't expect to spend a couple bucks for a phone app or less than $50.

Below are the different fields, units of measurements (how strong the field is), and suggested frequency ranges to look for when purchasing your meters:

AC Direct

- Measured by: V/m^2 (volts per meter squared), mV (millivolt)
- Conversions: 1,000 mV = 1 V/m
- Suggested range:
  - Should be able to measure up to 400,000 Hz or higher (to capture power line frequencies) and down to 1 V/m.
  - If you want to take measurements to turn off breaker switches, the meter needs to measure less than 1 V/m.
- Optional features: Ability to show dominant frequency bands in results (e.g., 50/60 Hz is an AC direct frequency band and should be the dominant band when measuring inside the house because that's what electricity is delivered at)

AC Magnetic

- Measured by: mG (milligauss) or nanotesla (nT)
- Conversions: 100 nT = 1 mG
- Suggested range: Ability to measure up to 400,000 Hz or higher (to capture power line frequencies) and less than 1 milligauss

- Optional: Ability to show dominant frequency bands, which is very helpful for detecting net current

Radio Frequency

- Measured by: $\mu W/m^2$ (microwatts per meter squared) or mW/m^2 (milliwatts per meter squared)
- Conversions:
    - $1\ \mu W/cm^2 = 10\ mW/m^2 = 10{,}000\ \mu W/m^2$
    - $.1\ \mu W/cm^2 = 1\ mW/m^2 = 1{,}000\ \mu W/m^2$
- Suggested range: Should measure down to megahertz (recommend 800 MHz or lower) to capture lower frequencies and at least to 3.3 GHz

  Note: Check and see if the meter mentions that LTE is taken into account for their measurements OR if the measurements need to have a multiplication factor if you are measuring LTE. This is especially important for some of the meters that have not updated their technology.
- Optional features:
    - Up to 6 GHz or higher (ideally)
    - Peak hold: Very helpful if you have smart meters, modems, routers, and other pulsed wireless sources both inside and outside of the home that send out bursts of radiation in milliseconds that are too quick to capture on an LCD display. This feature records the highest peak or burst and gives you an accurate picture of the radiation levels.
    - Pulsed versus Full: Allows you to take pulsed-only radio frequency readings and filter out the lower analog frequencies. In areas with a lot of strong Wi-Fi fields, this is less useful because the "full" readings will not vary much, if at all.

Tips for Taking Measurements

Once you have your instruments and start experimenting, I recommend:

- ❑ Always have a pen and paper, and record *everything*:
    - The type of field
    - The measurement
    - Location in the room or house
    - Date and time
    - For devices—if it was powered on or off or certain services were disabled
- ❑ Measure both inside and outside for all the fields
- ❑ Extra: If you don't have to worry about triggering an alarm system etc. take measurements with all breaker switches shut off (flip off each breaker switch individually, not the main)

Severity Categories and Your House

When it comes to "average" numbers and how good or bad your house is, unfortunately there isn't any regulation when it comes to EMF fields and biological (health) effects as they relate to nonionizing radiation.

The Building Biology principle takes a precautionary approach, and their guidelines are for *sleeping areas* only. This means the numbers are very conservative and what you will find in other shared areas and during the daytime hours are expected to be higher.

Below are the Building Biology guidelines for sleeping areas:

AC Electric (50–60 Hz)
Measurement: V/m (volts per meter)
No concern: <0.3
Slight concern: 0.3–1.5
Severe concern: 1.5–10
Extreme concern: >10

AC Magnetic (50–60 Hz)
Measurement: mG (milligauss)
No concern: <0.2
Slight concern: 0.2–1
Severe concern: 1–5
Extreme concern: >5

Radio Frequency
Measurement: µW/m^2 microwatts per meter squared
No concern: <0.1
Slight concern: 0.1–10
Severe concern: 10–1000
Extreme concern: >1000

Measurement: mW/m^2 milliwatts per meter squared
No concern: <0.0001
Slight concern: 0.0001–.01
Severe concern: .01–1
Extreme concern: >1

How to Get Your Safety Number

The safety number is a system I created that corresponds directly to the Building Biology categories. You can use this for each room (recommended) or for the entire house. Breaking out by room is the most accurate since different areas of a home can vary significantly.

No concern = 1
Slight concern = 2
Severe concern = 3
Extreme concern = 4

Step 1: Take measurements.

Walk through the room and measure all corners, the center of the room, and areas close to windows and doors. Do this for each of the fields.

Step 2: Categorize the measurements.

Categorize the measurements and assign a number 1–4 using the legend above for each of the fields.

Step 3: Average each field for each room.

Average the numbers for each field and each room to get your safety category. Now you have the safety category for each room.

Step 4: Average by floor or entire house (optional).

Use this data to average how you like—by floor or by the entire house.

Once you have your safety numbers, you'll be better informed not only about what's going on in your space, but also about what areas are higher priority based on the data.

EMF ROOM TRACKER AND SAFETY CATEGORY

Room: ____________________

AC Direct
Safety category
☐mV ☐V/m

AC Magnetic
Safety category
☐nT ☐mG

Radio Frequency
Safety category
☐μW/m² ☐mW/m²

Notes: ____________________

____

Room: ____________________

AC Direct
Safety category
☐mV ☐V/m

AC Magnetic
Safety category
☐nT ☐mG

Radio Frequency
Safety category
☐μW/m² ☐mW/m²

Notes: ____________________

____

CONCLUSION AND NEXT STEPS

Congratulations are in order—for YOU! You've finished the book, and that's no small feat, believe me!

This could mean you've either:

1. Read the book from start to finish and have completed clearing EMF fields in your house and creating your personal EMF survival plan, or you're still in the thick of everything and just haven't finished yet. Another congratulations to you!
2. You've skimmed through the book, zoomed to the content you're most interested in, and made some changes here and there but haven't made much progress.

If you're in the second group, you are definitely not alone. I've been guilty of reading the last part of a book first, so I totally get it.

But it's not helping your health!

And if you're already suffering, it's definitely not helping you get better.

So before you put this down and think about when you're going to finish your EMF project, I want you to do two things:

1. Make a note or put an actual sticky note where it makes sense for you to start, whether it's at the very beginning or where you last left off.
2. Schedule the time so it's set aside, whether it's fifteen minutes a day or an hour or two a week. Pick something that's actually doable—and remember that doable is usually completely different than "in the ideal world."

Keep chipping away until you've completed everything. Remember, even if you only take a few minutes a day, it's still progress, and continuous progress will eventually get you to the end.

HOW TO WORK WITH ME

Understanding EMF fields can be a daunting task, even after you learn all of the fields and start remediating your house, changing your technology habits, and supplementing your health.

In fact, even after students finish their in-person and remote training to become a certified Building Biologist and they've passed their exams, they *still* have one more big hoop to jump through before they're awarded certification.

We're paired up with a senior member of the organization to oversee our final project or thesis to make sure that we know our stuff and to be a resource if needed. In other words, it wasn't all done in a vacuum.

The most challenging part of clearing EMF fields if you're a newbie is knowing which option is the best, because you usually have a few different choices. That's why having the knowledge and experience of someone who specializes in EMFs at your disposal can help you choose which direction to take and make the process even more efficient.

If you're interested in working directly with me, having me speak at an event or run an EMF workshop, please email Connect@RisaSuzuki.com with the details of your request.

For more valuable information on EMF fields, articles, and tips, I invite you to join me at www.RisaSuzuki.com.

ABOUT THE AUTHOR

Risa Suzuki is a certified Building Biology Environmental Consultant who is committed to creating healthy spaces by testing and clearing EMFs and toxins from our everyday indoor environments. Prior to developing her own EMF sensitivities and becoming a Building Biologist, Risa enjoyed a successful career at Microsoft spanning more than twenty-five years. She knows firsthand the importance of balancing how we use technology and managing our health when it comes to EMF radiation.

Risa currently lives in Seattle and enjoys traveling to new places and spending time outdoors with her furry friend, Finn.

To learn more about her services and how she can help you, visit www.RisaSuzuki.com.

GRATITUDES

A very, very special and heartfelt shout-out to Susie Earl, who provided the wonderful information for the health and nutrition chapter. My deepest gratitude goes to her for intuitively saying, "So tell me about this book you haven't written," the first time we met. Thank you for being my accountability coach and rock-solid foundation. Thank you for believing in the importance of this work and getting this out for the people who need it, and for encouraging me in my moments of doubt. She is the CEO of Lux Solar, Founder of GirlOnFire Inspired Coaching, and Integrative Nutrition Health Coach, with two certificates from the Institute of Integrative Nutrition, specializing in the endocrine and lymphatic system, and a Certified Massage Therapist from National Holistic Institute. She studied family naturopathy at Clayton College of Natural Health, and is an author and speaker on weight, emotion, perfectionism release with essential oils, food as medicine, and bio-individual eating.

Thank you, thank you, David Musnick, Cathy Cohn, Angie Thompson, Raquel Chin-Quee Murrow, Sarah H., Kasia Kines, Lisa Fraley, Lotte Kragh, Rodika Tchi, Stephanie Brown, and Christine Zipps for taking time out of your very busy schedules to provide feedback, encouragement, and excitement along this journey.

Many thanks to Archangel Ink (that's YOU, Kristie, Jordan, and Paige!) and Lynda for your infinite wisdom and guidance in helping bring this book to the world. You gave it that extra polish and shine.

Dad and Diana, and Mom, so many thanks for supporting my desire to do some good in this world.

Lastly, to the powers that be, thank you for aligning everything perfectly at the perfect time.

PLEASE LEAVE A REVIEW

Thank you for reading this book. I hope it answered your EMF questions and gave you some relief with doable solutions. I also hope this book has started you down the path of remediating your home, changing your technology habits, and incorporating some of the natural solutions that will help you fight against the effects of EMF fields.

I have a small favor I'd like to request.

Would you take a moment to leave a review on Amazon? Here is a direct link to take you right to the reviews page:
https://RisaSuzuki.com/WTEReview

I would greatly appreciate it. I hope you'll share how this book helped you, believing that someone who reads the review may need it.

Thank you so much!

Risa

BIBLIOGRAPHY

Becker, Robert O. *Cross Currents: The Promise of Electromedicine, the Perils of Electropollution*. J.P. Tarcher/Penguin, 2004.

Berwick, Marianne, and Paolo Vineis. "Markers of DNA Repair and Susceptibility to Cancer in Humans: an Epidemiologic Review." *Journal of the National Cancer Institute* 92, no. 11 (2000): 874–897.

Blackman C. "Cell phone radiation: Evidence from ELF and RF studies supporting more inclusive risk identification and assessment." *Pathophysiology* 16, no. 2-3 (2009): 205–216.

Blank, Martin. *Overpowered: What Science Tells Us about the Dangers of Cell Phones and Other Wifi-Age Devices*. Seven Stories Press, 2014.

Blank, M and Goodman R. "DNA is a fractal antenna in electromagnetic fields." *International Journal of Radiation Biology* 87, no. 4 (2011): 409–415.

Carlo, Andrea Di, et al. "Chronic Electromagnetic Field Exposure Decreases HSP70 Levels and Lowers Cytoprotection." *Journal of Cellular Biochemistry* 84, no. 3 (2002): 447–454.

Carlo, George Louis, and Martin Schram. *Cell Phones: Invisible Hazards in the Wireless Age: an Insider's Alarming Discoveries about Cancer and Genetic Damage*. Basic Books, 2002.

Cherry, Neil. "EMF/EMR Reduces Melatonin in Animals and People." *Dr. Neil Cherry*. www.neilcherry.nz/.

Crofton, Kerry. *A Wellness Guide for the Digital Age: with Safer-Tech Solutions for All Things Wired & Wireless*. Global Wellbeing Books, 2014.

Gandhi, OP, et al. "Electromagnetic Absorption in the Human Head and Neck for Mobile Telephones at 835 and 1900 MHz." *IEEE Transactions on Microwave Theory and Techniques* 44, no. 10 (1996): 1884–1897.

Garcia, A. M, et al. "Occupational Exposure to Extremely Low Frequency Electric and Magnetic Fields and Alzheimer Disease: a Meta-Analysis." *International Journal of Epidemiology* 37, no. 2 (2008): 329–340.

Hardell, L. "Mobile Phones, Cordless Phones and the Risk for Brain Tumours." *International Journal of Oncology* 35, no. 01 (2009). doi:10.3892/ijo_00000307.

Hardell, Lennart, et al. "Case-Control Study of the Association between Malignant Brain Tumours Diagnosed between 2007 and 2009 and Mobile and Cordless Phone Use." *International Journal of Oncology* 43, no. 6 (2013): 1833–1845.

Johnson, Jon. "Can apple cider vinegar help treat cancer?" *MedicalNewsToday*. Oct. 24, 2018. www.medicalnewstoday.com/articles/323439.php.

Khurana, VG, *et al.* "Epidemiological evidence for a health risk from mobile phone base stations." *International Journal of Occupational Health* 16, no. 3 (2010): 263–267.

Klinghardt, D. "Mercury Detoxification: Perpetuating Factors, Problems and Obstacles." *Klinghardt Academy*. www.klinghardtacademy.com/Articles/Mercury-Detoxification-Perpetuating-Factors-Problems-and-Obstacles.html.

Lee, Lita. *Radiation Protection Manual*, 3rd ed. Lita Lee, 1991.

Lerchi, A., et al. "Pineal gland 'magnetosensitivity' to static magnetic fields is a consequence of induced electric currents (eddy currents)." *Journal of Pineal Research* 10 (1991): 109–116.

Lönn, Stefan, et al. "Mobile Phone Use and the Risk of Acoustic Neuroma." *Epidemiology* 15, no. 6 (2004): 653–659.

Milham, Samuel. *Dirty Electricity: Electrification and the Diseases of Civilization*. IUniverse Inc., 2012.

Oschman, James. *Energy Medicine*. London: Churchill Livingstone, 2000.

Phillips JL, NP Singh, H. Lai. "Electromagnetic fields and DNA damage." *Pathophysiology* 16, no. 2-3 (2009): 79–88.

Qualcomm Technologies. "What can we do with 5G NR Spectrum Sharing that isn't possible today?" December 13, 2017. https://www.qualcomm.com/media/documents/files/new-3gpp-effort-on-nr-in-unlicensed-spectrum-expands-5g-to-new-areas.pdf.

Reese, Camilla and Magda Havas, *Public Health SOS: The Shadow Side of the Wireless Revolution*. CreateSpace, 2009.

Salford, Leif G., A. Brun, K. Sturesson, JL Eberhardt, BR Persson. "Permeability of the Blood-Brain Barrier Induced by 915 MHz Electromagnetic Radiation, Continuous Wave and Modulated at 8, 16, 50, and 200Hz." *Microscopy Research and Technique* 27, no. 6 (1994): 535–542.

Savitz, David A., et al. "Magnetic Field Exposure and Neurodegenerative Disease Mortality among Electric Utility Workers." *Epidemiology* 9, no. 4 (1998): 398–404.

Schecter, Steven. *Fighting Radiation and Chemical Pollutants with Food, Herbs, and Vitamins*. Vitality Ink, 1990.

Singer, Katie. *An Electronic Silent Spring*. Portal Books, 2014.

Sobel, E., et al. "Elevated Risk of Alzheimer's Disease among Workers with Likely Electromagnetic Field Exposure." *Neurology* 47, no. 6 (1996): 1477–1481.

Tainio, Bruce. "Frequency." *EnergicX*. www.energicxusa.com/frequency-of-human-body/.

"Thousands of Satellites Set to Launch for 5G," Worldhealth.net, January 8, 2019, https://www.worldhealth.net/news/thousands-satellites-set-launch-5g/.

Tice, Raymond R., et al. "Genotoxicity of Radiofrequency Signals. I. Investigation of DNA Damage and Micronuclei Induction in Cultured Human Blood Cells." *Bioelectromagnetics* 23, no. 2 (2002): 113–126.

Wertheimer, Nancy, and Ed Leeper. "Electrical Wiring Configurations And Childhood Cancer." *American Journal of Epidemiology* 109, no. 3 (1979): 273–284.

ENDNOTES

1 Martin Blank, *Overpowered: What Science Tells Us about the Dangers of Cell Phones and Other Wifi-Age Devices* (Seven Stories Press, 2014), 63.

2 Kerry Crofton, *A Wellness Guide for the Digital Age: with Safer-Tech Solutions for All Things Wired & Wireless* (Global Wellbeing Books, 2014), 38.

3 Blank, *Overpowered*, 85–86.

4 Crofton, *A Wellness Guide for the Digital Age*, 36–37.

5 George Louis Carlo and Martin Schram, *Cell Phones: Invisible Hazards in the Wireless Age: an Insider's Alarming Discoveries about Cancer and Genetic Damage* (Basic Books, 2002).

6 Leif G. Salford et al., "Permeability of the Blood-Brain barrier Induced by 915 MHz Electromagnetic Radiation, Continuous Wave and Modulated at 8, 16, 50, and 200Hz," *Microscopy Research and Technique* 27, no. 6 (1994): 535–542, doi: 10.1002/jemt.107027068.

7 Crofton, *A Wellness Guide for the Digital Age*.

8 M. Blank and R. Goodman, "DNA is a fractal antenna in electromagnetic fields," *International Journal of Radiation Biology* 87, no. 4 (2011): 409–415.

9 Blank, *Overpowered*.

10 Crofton, *A Wellness Guide for the Digital Age*, 33.

11 Andrea Di Carlo et al., "Chronic Electromagnetic Field Exposure Decreases HSP70 Levels and Lowers Cytoprotection," *Journal of Cellular Biochemistry* 84, no. 3 (2002): 447–454, doi:10.1002/jcb.10036.

12 Blank, *Overpowered*, 61–62.

13 JL Phillips, NP Singh, H. Lai, "Electromagnetic fields and DNA damage," *Pathophysiology* 16, no. 2-3 (2009): 79–88.

14 Bruce Tainio, "Frequency," *EnergicX*, www.energicxusa.com/frequency-of-human-body/.

15 Robert O Becker, *Cross Currents: The Promise of Electromedicine, the Perils of Electropollution* (J.P. Tarcher/Penguin, 2004).

16 Marianne Berwick and Paolo Vineis, "Markers of DNA Repair and Susceptibility to Cancer in Humans: an Epidemiologic Review," *Journal of the National Cancer Institute* 92, no. 11 (2000): 874–897, doi:10.1093/jnci/92.11.874.

17 Raymond R. Tice et al., "Genotoxicity of Radiofrequency Signals. I. Investigation of DNA Damage and Micronuclei Induction in Cultured Human Blood Cells." *Bioelectromagnetics* 23, no. 2 (2002): 113–126, doi:10.1002/bem.104.

18 Phillips et al., "Electromagnetic fields and DNA damage," 79–88.

19 Samuel Milham, *Dirty Electricity: Electrification and the Diseases of Civilization*, IUniverse Inc., 2012.

20 Lennart Hardell et al., "Case-Control Study of the Association between Malignant Brain Tumours Diagnosed between 2007 and 2009 and Mobile and Cordless Phone Use." *International Journal of Oncology* 43, no. 6 (2013): 1833–1845, doi:10.3892/ijo.2013.2111.

21 Stefan Lönn et al., "Mobile Phone Use and the Risk of Acoustic Neuroma," *Epidemiology* 15, no. 6 (2004): 653–659, doi:10.1097/01.ede.0000142519.00772.bf.

22 Nancy Wertheimer and Ed Leeper, "Electrical Wiring Configurations And Childhood Cancer," *American Journal of Epidemiology* 109, no. 3 (1979): 273–284, doi:10.1093/oxfordjournals.aje.a112681.

23 E. Sobel et al., "Elevated Risk of Alzheimer's Disease among Workers with Likely Electromagnetic Field Exposure," *Neurology* 47, no. 6 (1996): 1477–1481, doi:10.1212/wnl.47.6.1477.

24 A. M Garcia et al., "Occupational Exposure to Extremely Low Frequency Electric and Magnetic Fields and Alzheimer Disease: a Meta-Analysis," *International Journal of Epidemiology* 37, no. 2 (2008): 329–340, doi:10.1093/ije/dym295.

25 Blank, *Overpowered*, 82–83.

26 David A. Savitz et al., "Magnetic Field Exposure and Neurodegenerative Disease Mortality among Electric Utility Workers," *Epidemiology* 9, no. 4 (1998): 398–404, doi:10.1097/00001648-199807000-00009.

27 Blank, *Overpowered*, 82–83.

28 Carlo and Schram, *Cell Phones: Invisible Hazards in the Wireless Age*, 218–219.

29 C. Blackman, "Cell phone radiation: Evidence from ELF and RF studies supporting more inclusive risk identification and assessment," *Pathophysiology* 16, no. 2-3 (2009): 205–216.

30 A. Lerchi et al., "Pineal gland 'magnetosensitivity' to static magnetic fields is a consequence of induced electric currents (eddy currents)," *Journal*

of Pineal Research 10 (1991): 109–116, doi: 10.1111/j.1600-079X.1991. tboo826l.x.

31 Neil Cherry, "EMF/EMR Reduces Melatonin in Animals and People," *Dr. Neil Cherry*, www.neilcherry.nz/.

32 Crofton, *A Wellness Guide for the Digital Age*, 87.

33 D. Klinghardt, "Mercury Detoxification: Perpetuating Factors, Problems and Obstacles," *Klinghardt Academy*, www.klinghardtacademy.com/Articles/Mercury-Detoxification-Perpetuating-Factors-Problems-and-Obstacles.html.

34 Carlo and Schram, *Cell Phones: Invisible Hazards in the Wireless Age*, 216–217.

35 OP Gandhi et al., "Electromagnetic Absorption in the Human Head and Neck for Mobile Telephones at 835 and 1900 MHz," *IEEE Transactions on Microwave Theory and Techniques* 44, no. 10 (1996): 1884–1897, doi:10.1109/22.539947.

36 Gandhi et al., "Electromagnetic Absorption in the Human Head and Neck for Mobile Telephones at 835 and 1900 MHz," 1884–1897.

37 Gandhi et al., "Electromagnetic Absorption in the Human Head and Neck for Mobile Telephones at 835 and 1900 MHz," 1884–1897.

38 Hardell et al., "Case-Control Study of the Association between Malignant Brain Tumours Diagnosed between 2007 and 2009 and Mobile and Cordless Phone Use," 1833–1845.

39 L. Hardell, "Mobile Phones, Cordless Phones and the Risk for Brain Tumours," *International Journal of Oncology* 35, no. 01 (2009), doi:10.3892/ijo_00000307.

40 James Oschman, *Energy Medicine* (London: Churchill Livingstone, 2000).

41 Katie Singer, *An Electronic Silent Spring* (Portal Books, 2014), 60.

42 Singer, *An Electronic Silent Spring*, 60.

43 Singer, *An Electronic Silent Spring*, 60.

44 Singer, *An Electronic Silent Spring*, 60.

45 Singer, *An Electronic Silent Spring*, 60.

46 Singer, *An Electronic Silent Spring*, 60.

47 Qualcomm Technologies, "What can we do with 5G NR Spectrum Sharing that isn't possible today?" December 13, 2017. https://www.qualcomm.com/media/documents/files/new-3gpp-effort-on-nr-in-unlicensed-spectrum-expands-5g-to-new-areas.pdf.

48 "Thousands of Satellites Set to Launch for 5G," Worldhealth.net, January 8, 2019, https://www.worldhealth.net/news/thousands-satellites-set-launch-5g/.

49 See https://en.wikipedia.org/wiki/Internet_of_things.

50 VG Khurana *et al.,* "Epidemiological evidence for a health risk from mobile phone base stations," *International Journal of Occupational Health* July–Sept. 16, no. 3 (2010): 263–267.

51 Blank, *Overpowered*, 72–74.

52 Springer, *An Electronic Silent Spring*, 97.

53 Camilla Reese and Magda Havas, *Public Health SOS: The Shadow Side of the Wireless Revolution* (CreateSpace, 2009), 41.

54 Springer, *An Electronic Silent Spring*, 91.

55 Jon Johnson, "Can apple cider vinegar help treat cancer?" *MedicalNewsToday*, Oct. 24, 2018, www.medicalnewstoday.com/articles/323439.php.

56 Lita Lee, Ph.D., *Radiation Protection Manual*, 3rd ed. (Lita Lee, 1991).

57 Steven Schecter, *Fighting Radiation and Chemical Pollutants with Food, Herbs, and Vitamins* (Vitality Ink, 1990).

58 For more on how to combat EMFs with the right nutrition, check out these resources:

Institute of Integrative Nutrition, www.integrativenutrition.com; HealthlineMedia UK Ltd, Brighton, UK;

Staying Healthy with Nutrition by Elson M. Haas; Safespaceprotectin/healthy-tips/the-anti-radian-diet;

Carotene and Retinol Efficacy Trial (CARET), https://epi.grants.cancer.gov/Consortia/members/caret.html;

"Everything you need to know about emu oil," https://www.medicalnewstoday.com/articles/315535.php.

Made in the USA
Monee, IL
19 December 2019